SPACECRAFT AND MISSILES OF THE WORLD, 1966

ALSO BY
WILLIAM E. HOWARD AND JAMES BAAR

POLARIS!
COMBAT MISSILEMAN
SPACECRAFT AND MISSILES OF THE WORLD, 1962

SPACECRAFT AND MISSILES OF THE WORLD, 1966

WILLIAM E. HOWARD AND JAMES BAAR

HARCOURT, BRACE & WORLD, INC., NEW YORK

Mariner IV heads for Mars.
—General Dynamics photograph

AUTHORS' NOTE

Every effort has been made to make certain that all of the information contained in this edition of **Spacecraft and Missiles** is the most accurate obtainable given the increasingly tight bounds of United States and foreign military security. As for the material on Soviet missiles, it is considered to be the best available in the West outside of the official intelligence community. Relatively little technical information on Soviet missiles and spacecraft has ever been released by the Soviet Union.

Cape Kennedy, foreground, from 108 miles up, looking
south from a Gemini capsule.

—NASA photograph

CONTENTS

Scale model of Lunar Excursion Module standing on the moon with earth in the background.
—NASA photograph

1

MAN REACHES FOR THE MOON

THE TARGET

Mean distance from earth:	238,000 mi.
Diameter:	2,160 mi.
Atmosphere:	None.
Water:	None.
Surface temperature:	+212° to −270° F.
Surface:	Vacuum-packed dust.
Features:	Craters, mountains, plains.
Origin:	Unknown.

Lucian of Samosata, rhetorician and brilliant Greek satirist, was one of the first men to visualize a trip to the moon, and preserve the idea in writing. In his parody *True History,* dating back to A.D. 160, Lucian tells how a giant windstorm seizes a sailboat off the Pillars of Hercules and hurls it hundreds of miles into the sky. A week later, the voyagers are thrown up on the moon. They soon are helping Moon men battle Sun men for possession of Venus. After many more adventures, the men sail back to Earth, stopping off at "Lamptown" in "Cloud Cuckooland" for a while, and finally put down in the ocean, where they are swallowed by a sea monster.

Certain parallels may be drawn with this grandfather science-fiction yarn now that man, eighteen centuries later, actually is endeavoring to walk upon the moon. Astronauts will start out with the aid of a great "wind," only harnessed inside a huge rocket. En route, their spaceship will glide through the heavens as silently as a sailboat. The entire half-million-mile round trip will take a week (not just the outward leg). The spaceship will glow like a bright "lamp" in the sky as it returns to the atmosphere at a meteor-fast 25,000 miles per hour. And the American Apollo lunar craft, if the flight plan works out, will splash down in the Pacific Ocean.

Modern telescopes, radar and close-up photographs by U.S. Ranger spacecraft have removed the possibility of Moon men. The moon is a small, dead planet apparently barren of all life. No winds stir its silent mountain peaks and dusty plains, ravaged by billions of years of cosmic shelling, for there is no air. Clutched in a vacuum and bathed by dangerous radiation and whizzing meteoroids, it is indeed an exceedingly treacherous place for explorers to venture to. Lucian, of course, didn't know this.

Neither could he foresee what eventually would impel men to undertake so hazardous a trip of their own accord. But it is at least an interesting coincidence that this ancient writer did imagine a monumental conflict between men over the domination of another world. He had the right motive but the wrong planet.

Today, the United States and Russia are both reaching outward into space as contestants. They are extending to this hostile realm the great ideological struggle that has divided East and West

1

since World War II. Mastery of space is proving difficult, and it may — or may not — decide who rules earth. But being first to explore the moon has become a symbol of who is winning the contest. It was made so when the late President John F. Kennedy stood before a joint session of Congress on May 25, 1961, and declared:

"I believe that this nation should commit itself to the goal, before this decade is out, of landing a man on the moon and returning him safely to earth. No single space project in this period will be more impressive to mankind or more important for the long-range exploration of space. And none will be so difficult or expensive to accomplish."

This momentous decision, quickly accepted by Congress, was precipitated by Russia's bold conquest of gravity. The U.S.S.R. had abruptly turned empty space, 100 to 200 miles above the earth, into a Cold War testing ground of technological prowess — and a potential threat to the security of the free world. Barely six weeks before, on April 12, 1961, the Soviets had launched the first man, Major Yuri Gagarin, into orbit, capping a string of spectacular "firsts" that had begun with Sputnik I on October 4, 1957, the satellite that had whipped open the curtain on the Space Age and stunned the world.

Clearly, the United States was losing what had become a "space race." Project Mercury, a single-seat spaceship, had been started in 1958. But it was too little and too late. The young President, four months in office, turned to his advisory National Aeronautics and Space Council, headed by the man who shortly would succeed him in office, Vice President Lyndon B. Johnson. The council's answer: If we try, we can overtake the Russians at the moon.

Up to this point, the situation seemed clear-cut. Nearly all Americans assumed that the *manned* exploration of space was important and inevitable; that Soviet spaceships whizzing over New York, Chicago and Tecumcari could be used to spit out nuclear weapons. The Russians had thrown down a challenge; it was unthinkable not to accept it.

Soon, however, severe doubts began to shake the embryo Project Apollo like the ague. Critics pointed out that if a military threat existed in space, it was near earth, not at the moon. (See Chapter 3.) Prominent scientists complained that they were not consulted when the decision was made and attacked the vast engineering effort as almost wholly lacking in scientific merit. Instru-

ments sent into space, they said, could see, hear and feel far more cheaply and with much greater accuracy and speed than fragile man, who could go aloft only when wrapped in a protective cocoon fabricated at enormous expense. However, despite continued criticism, in January 1963, the Space Sciences Board of the National Academy of Sciences, perhaps the nation's most influential body of scientific opinion, dropped its objections and hailed the space flight as "one of man's truly great adventures."

In Congress, though, NASA's ballooning expenditures were eyed with increasing trepidation. Some lawmakers denounced the huge outlays as "moon madness," acidly pointing out there was no guarantee the Soviets were heading for the moon. The United States could well have put itself in a one-horse race. But NASA continued to get almost all the money it requested.

The "race" took a bizarre turn in September 1963, when President Kennedy, in an obvious political ploy before the United Nations General Assembly, invited the Russians to join the United States in the conquest of the moon. The proposal was regarded as incredible by American spacemen. Three months later, following Kennedy's assassination, President Johnson renewed the offer. The Russians turned it down.

While debaters fumed, the world advanced steadily into the Space Age. It became rapidly apparent that the Soviet Union had embarked on a major onslaught of the cosmos, with both men and instruments to explore the planets. Their program was well conceived, well organized and well funded. With a rocket three times more powerful than the biggest United States booster, they proceeded to open up a commanding lead in manned space flight experience. Although, curiously enough, after managing to produce the first muddy photographs of the moon's backside in 1959, Soviet scientists encountered serious trouble in further exploration of the moon and planets during the next five years, finally obtaining some more moon pictures in 1965.

Gagarin's historic one-orbit flight in Vostok I was followed by five more Vostoks in 1961, 1962 and 1963. All created a sensation, overshadowing America's Mercury spacecraft, which had a very limited endurance in space. Working out of a spaceport at Tyura Tam, Kazakh, just east of the Aral Sea, the Soviets on August 11, 1962, orbited Andrian Nikolayev, and on the very next day sent

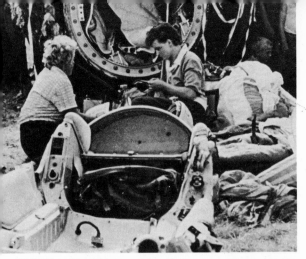

Valentina Tereshkova, right, first space woman, examines the Vostok VI which carried her on a three-day flight in June 1963. Ejection seat is in foreground.
—Novosti Press Agency photograph

up a second cosmonaut, Pavel Popovich. Their two ships at one point came within 600 yards of each other and, if they had been equipped with the proper controls, probably could have linked up or rendezvoused in orbit. As it was, Nikolayev remained aloft for almost four days and his wingman, three days. Valeri Bykovsky, in Vostok V, however, soon set a new endurance mark, going aloft on June 14, 1963, and staying five days. He was followed two days after takeoff by Valentina Tereshkova, the first woman cosmonaut, who stuck it out three days.

The United States, in the interim, succeeded in putting up four astronauts in Mercury capsules. Lieutenant Colonel John Glenn was the first, making America's space debut with a three-orbit ride lasting just under five hours on February 20, 1962. Flights of five and nine hours were recorded by Scott Carpenter and Walter Schirra in 1962. Then, on May 15, 1963, Gordon Cooper took a flight lasting 34 hours to conclude the program.

At the end of 1963, the windup of "first-generation" spaceships, the score stood: Russia — 383 man-hours in space; the United States — 53 man-hours in space.

While exciting as high trapeze acts and highly useful as engineering experience, the ten space flights appeared to prove little scientifically other than that man could function in the gravity-free environment of space without ill effects for short periods of time. Scientists had already predicted such would be the case. There were, however, some medical danger signals. Gherman Titov, Russia's second cosmonaut, became nauseated on his 17-orbit flight in 1961 when he suffered an inner-ear disturbance that made him dizzy. The Soviets said the condition could be averted in the future by special training. American doctors noticed that Mercury astronauts did sustain some minute losses of bone calcium, which they attributed to weightlessness and the pooling of blood in their legs. The Russians, chary at first with their medical data, later said they found much the same evidence.

The first phase of manned space flight had struck the world's fancy and the two competitors pushed on: the Soviets with an enlarged Vostok called Voskhod; the United States with an enlarged Mercury called Gemini.

Voskhod turned out to be a real surprise. The first one, orbited on October 13, 1964, contained three men — the pilot, a physician, and a spaceship designer — the world's first multiman spaceship. The ship stayed up a full day. Voskhod II was an even bigger jolt. On March 18, 1965, while completing his first circuit of the globe, Aleksei A. Leonov, a 30-year-old Red Air Force lieutenant colonel, opened the hatch of the spacecraft and, wearing a spacesuit with some oxygen tanks

Russia's Alexei Leonov taking man's first walk in space March 18, 1965.
—Tass photograph from UPI

strapped to his back, stepped out into the void. Holding on to a tether tied to Voskhod II, Leonov floated freely in space for 10 minutes, the first man ever to do so. A co-pilot in the two-man ship televised the feat back to astonished Muscovites.

Leonov's brave acrobatics were more than a stunt, said Russia's "chief designer of spaceships," a man (or men) who long had assumed the cloak of complete anonymity. The Soviets would employ space-floating cosmonauts to assist in the joining of structures into space stations and probably to refuel ships bound for the moon. This was an entirely different technique from that being developed by the United States, but possibly a much faster means of accomplishing an around-the-moon flight or a lunar landing.

In the first five years of manned space operations, the Soviets consistently led the United States. With great daring they wrung the most out of their equipment.

Russia opened the Space Age with a rocket that was originally designed as an intercontinental ballistic missile, capable of hurling a nuclear warhead weighing 10,000 pounds at the United States. It is true, however, that Soviet scientists would not have developed this 800,000-pound-thrust monster if they had not been backward technically in the fabrication of atomic weapons. They were stuck with a 10,000-pound warhead, the heft of the Hiroshima bomb.

The United States, on the other hand, was on the way to a 3,000-pound warhead packing a hydrogen bomb when it started building its first ICBM, the Atlas, in 1954. As a result, the Atlas purposely was designed for only 360,000 pounds of thrust, and when it was converted into a space booster the United States was left with a severe weight-lifting handicap. This spelled the difference in the manned space race.

The Soviet space booster, reported to have a cluster of five rocket engines in the first stage, underwent major improvements over the years. By lengthening fuel tanks, increasing engine power, and adding high-efficiency upper stages, the thrust rating was hiked to about 1,200,000 pounds for Vostok, and 1,430,000 pounds for Voskhod.

Voskhods weighed 11,700 pounds and were roomy enough to allow cosmonauts to leave their couches and float about. Voskhod II was able to accommodate an air lock by the elimination of one seat.

In July 1965, the Soviets unveiled what ap-peared to be a powerful new rocket when they orbited an unmanned "space station" — Proton I, weighing 27,000 pounds. The booster was rated at 2.5 million pounds thrust. It was expected to be used in their lunar expedition.

Gemini, a two-seater ship, was invented late in 1961 by NASA as a means of racking up some badly needed flight experience. At first, the craft was to be little more than an expanded Mercury capsule. But the space agency decided to "sophisticate" Gemini's systems and missions, including rendezvous and docking maneuvers, causing an 18-month delay and doubling the program's cost to 1.3 billion dollars. The refinements, though, seemed worth it when astronauts Virgil I. ("Gus") Grissom and John W. Young finally took off aboard a Titan II rocket on March 23, 1965.

Astronauts John W. Young, foreground, and Virgil I. "Gus" Grissom in their spacecraft just before launch of Gemini-Titan III on a three-orbit mission, March 23, 1965.

—NASA photograph

Astronaut Edward H. White II floats in space, secured to Gemini IV spacecraft by umbilical line and tether.
—NASA photograph

In a three-orbit tryout of the 7,800-pound Gemini, partially eclipsed by Leonov's space "walk" only five days before, they proved nevertheless that the United States was the first to develop a maneuverable manned spacecraft. Assisted by small rocket thrusters located around the sides and a 57-pound computer in the cockpit, Grissom skillfully piloted the ship through a series of orbital changes. The flight signaled a new American initiative.

Ten weeks later, on June 3, 1965, Major Edward H. White stepped out of his Gemini IV 100 miles above Hawaii and more than duplicated Leonov's feat. He remained on a tether for 23 minutes and, for part of the time, propelled himself about in space with a small gun that squirted compressed oxygen. It was a quick answer to the Russians, since EVA — extravehicular activity — was not part of the U.S. plan for getting to the moon. NASA just happened to be ready. White and his command pilot, Major James A. McDivitt, then remained in orbit four days.

Worries about man's ability to endure physically a week-long round trip to the moon were dispelled in the flight of Gemini V. Colonel Cooper, making his second flight, and Commander Charles Conrad, Jr., captured the orbital endurance record by staying aloft almost a full eight days, starting on August 21, 1965. They returned in top physical condition, managing to offset the debilitating ef-

fects of weightlessness by exercising with a stretch cord and drinking plenty of water. The flight put the U.S. ahead of Russia at that point in total man-hours aloft, 639 to 507, though not in spacecraft hours flown.

The program's next objective was to practice the extremely difficult feat of rendezvousing two ships in orbit and physically linking them up — a critical maneuver in rescuing Apollo astronauts from the moon. Both the U.S. and Russia experienced considerable difficulty in early attempts, using satellites and manned spacecraft as targets. The problem was in the precision timing, first to launch the ships into identical orbital planes (along the same angle with true north) and, secondly, to phase their orbits so they would come together.

Agenas equipped with docking collars were the main Gemini targets in flights scheduled through early 1967. Various experiments, meantime, were proving that spaceships made extraordinary observational platforms. The Gemini pilots were able to spot "dark" objects—satellites, burned-out rockets and other man-made space debris — indicating that some day it might be possible to intercept a hostile craft in orbit. They could see missiles, ships and aircraft moving far below them and they returned with finely detailed pictures of the earth's surface taken with telephoto lenses. Thus, they blazed a trail for military spacemen as they pushed for the moon.

Gemini rescue at sea is aided by frogmen, who place flotation collar around the capsule and help transfer astronauts to hovering helicopter.
—NASA photograph

The pacing item for Apollo was rocket power.

If there was indeed a race to put men on the moon, America's chances of being first rode on the successful development of a 280-foot, three-stage booster, the Saturn V. The whole program was built around this rocket, scheduled for its first test flight in 1967.

When Kennedy set the nation's sail for the moon, only one large space booster was being built, the Saturn I, a 1.5-million-pound-thrust vehicle composed of eight rockets with virtually the same rating as Russia's Voskhod carrier. Exhaustive engineering studies convinced NASA that it would be too risky to use Saturn I's to assemble a moon ship in earth orbit. They did not reckon on the proficiency which could be obtained with maneuvering spacecraft. But they reasoned, perhaps correctly, that an astronaut would be restricted in the work he could perform while weightless; that even tightening a bolt could send him spinning helplessly. Moreover, a complicated spaceship could not be tested adequately or simple repairs made while in orbit except with great difficulty. It was much better, in the interests of reliability and safety, to do everything on the ground.

The question then came down to how big a spacecraft was needed and how big a rocket to send it moonward. At that time, too, a rocket engine able to generate 1.5 million pounds of thrust by itself was being developed — the F-1. The calculators figured that a rocket made of five F-1's, generating 7.5 million pounds of thrust in the "basement" stage, plus two more stages with a total of 1.2 million pounds of thrust, could boost 90,000 pounds to the moon, or roughly the weight of Columbus' smallest ship, the *Nina*.

This seemed like enough for a three-man spaceship, supplies and fuel until NASA looked at the problem of getting on — and off — the moon. It was found the craft couldn't carry fuel for the rockets to lower the men gently through the vacuum above the moon's surface and still have enough for the return blastoff. Supplying Apollo with extra fuel through an earth-orbital rendezvous before heading for the moon was briefly considered and rejected. Static electricity could cause an explosion during fuel transfer and the risk of collision was high.

The solution: bring along a small spacecraft that could land two men. It could cast off like a lifeboat from the mother ship, put down on the moon and take off, eliminating a landing by Apollo.

This scheme was adopted, although its success depended upon the returning explorers' making a rendezvous in lunar orbit with the mother ship. If they missed, they would die.

NASA left the public entirely out of the long engineering debate. Officials said they were afraid the Russians would steal the best ideas.

When it finally revealed the flight plan, NASA contended that the scheme offered real safety features. The critical rendezvous could be practiced in earth orbit and both the lunar excursion module (LEM), or "Bug" as it was nicknamed, and the Apollo would be maneuverable. If the "Bug" became stranded, the third astronaut, in the mother ship, could come to the rescue.

Agena satellite, left, and Gemini practice docking on the ground at Cape Kennedy before attempting a rendezvous in space.

—NASA photograph

The space agency busily set in motion elaborate industrial plans to get the task under way and somehow avoided discussion of the truly major drawback to the whole grand concept: virtually every piece of equipment would have to be built from scratch.

Even the Saturn I, which had made its flight debut in 1961, couldn't help. A heavier version, the Saturn I-B, had to be developed to lift a partially-fueled Apollo into earth orbit. Why Saturn I, which could have put 5,000 pounds on the moon, was never given an assignment — except to orbit a micrometeoroid-hunting satellite called Pegasus — remained a mystery. With the right payload of instruments, it might have been able to bring back a sample of moon dust long before anyone set foot there.

The mission of the Saturn I-B, in the 1966-1968 time period, was to send Apollo spaceships into

Test pilot in pressure suit stands before full-scale mock-up of Lunar Excursion Module.

—NASA photograph

was constructed to land only on the airless moon. It does not have a protective heat shield for piercing the earth's atmosphere. So, if the occupants missed connections with the Apollo, they would be stranded in space and perish.

Fifteen Saturn V's were ordered by NASA. Five to eight flights were allotted for determining that the huge rocket was reliable enough to put men aboard. (By comparison, there were more than 100 flights of the Atlas as an ICBM and space booster before Mercury astronauts took a ride.) Advanced engineering and reliability techniques, the space agency claimed, could make the Saturn V safe with such limited flight experience.

The risks, nevertheless, remained great. Just sitting on the launch pad, loaded with about 5 million pounds of kerosene, liquid oxygen and liquid hydrogen, the Saturn V was a great powder keg containing an explosive force equivalent to a small atomic bomb. But if the hazards were mastered, Apollo engineers believed an attempt at a circumlunar flight could be made on the twelfth or thirteenth launch with a moon landing following on the next shot.

Barring some major disaster, NASA hopes to take off for the moon in late 1969 or early 1970. The flight plan calls for the great expedition to be accomplished in this sequence:

earth orbit. At altitudes of 100 to 200 miles, astronauts would begin practicing on the same equipment they would fly to the moon and, at the same time, pick up more space flight experience. The key objective here was learning how to flip around the Apollo command and service modules (the latter contains a 22,000-pound-thrust rocket, electrical power units and other supplies) and dock them to the "Bug," which is carried in the booster's top stage. Eight to ten manned flights were planned for this phase.

Manned flights of the Apollo-Saturn V, set for 1968-1970, were intended further to qualify the equipment and the astronauts. In some flights two astronauts would crawl into the "Bug" following an earth-orbital linkup with Apollo. They would cast off, fly around and then rendezvous again with the Apollo. Potentially, this was one of the most hazardous practice maneuvers. The "Bug"

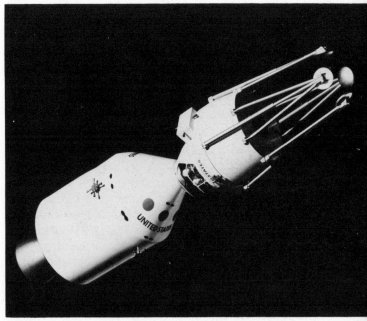

How Apollo will look en route to the moon. Lunar Excursion Module, right, is joined to Command Module shortly after leaving earth orbit.

—NASA photograph

7

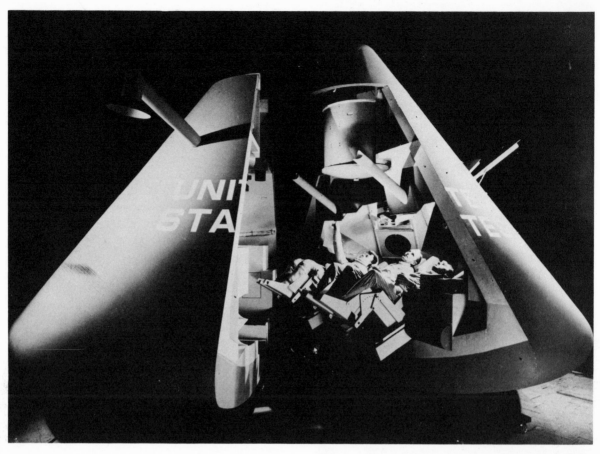

Cross-section of three-manned Apollo spacecraft model.
—NASA photograph

Strapped into padded couches, the three explorers will be sent into a 200-mile-high earth orbit in a trajectory similar to those flown by Mercury and Gemini capsules. After one or two circuits, during which data is fed from ground tracking stations into Apollo's inertial guidance computer, the Saturn V's third stage will be reignited to accelerate the craft to 25,000 miles per hour on a course for the moon. Shortly after reaching this velocity and "escaping" the earth's gravitation, the Apollo command and service modules will be separated from the rocket by the spaceship commander. He will turn the spaceship around and dock nose to nose with the "Bug." A structural connection will be made and the third stage detached from the "Bug" with explosive bolts. Then the whole weird-appearing rig will be turned around again and proceed to the moon.

The astronauts will not aim directly at the moon, of course, because it is moving at 2,160 miles per hour. They will have to "lead" it like a

duck hunter, making various corrections with the service module's 22,000-pound-thrust rocket to stay on an intercept course. During the outward leg of the journey, lasting about 65 hours, the moon will be traveling about 140,000 miles in its orbit. The Apollo's speed will vary, too. After its final five minutes of powered flight away from earth it will gradually slow to about 3,000 miles per hour. Later, as it comes under the moon's gravity, the speed will pick up to more than 6,000 miles per hour.

The intercept will be made by passing in front of the moon at an altitude of about 100 miles and then turning on the service rocket to slow the spacecraft down to 3,600 miles per hour. This is the speed necessary for a lunar orbit.

An attempt at a landing will come after the Apollo has made a couple of trips around the moon and the astronauts have their bearings. They will have highly detailed maps of the intended landing site, prepared from Ranger and Lunar

Orbiter photographs and possibly from a previous Apollo circumlunar flight. There are hopes that a Surveyor spacecraft "soft landed" earlier will signal the presence of lunar terrain strong enough to bear the 30,000-pound "Bug."

All three astronauts will don spacesuits, the two explorers' suits built somewhat like armor to maintain pressure inside yet allow them freedom of movement. The suits also will shield them from radiation and meteoroids on the moon. The two will then enter the "Bug" through a hatch and, after assuring themselves that the craft is in working order, cast off. They will drop to about 10 miles above the lunar surface, then fire the descent engine to glide down to an altitude of 500 to 1,000 feet. At this point they will hover for a few seconds and guide the spacecraft laterally until they are over the landing area.

The final descent will be straight down with the "Bug" hitting the lunar surface with a hard bump.

If the surface crumbles beneath them, or proves to be deep dust, the astronauts will immediately jettison the descent engine and kick on the ascent rocket to escape back into lunar orbit.

For all the enormous difficulty in finally making

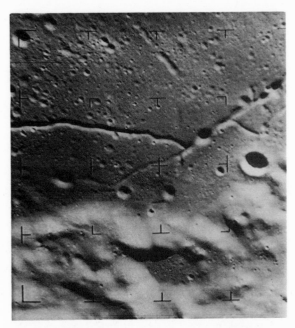

Heavily pocked surface of the moon—a hazard for explorers—is apparent in closeup taken by Ranger IX.
—NASA photograph

it to the moon, however, the exploration itself will be very brief — just 24 hours on the first trip. In that time the explorers will venture one at a time from the "Bug" wearing "bio-paks" on their backs to sustain them. They will move carefully, keeping in sight of the spacecraft and in constant radio contact. They will carry a small TV camera to show what they find to a waiting world.

The first question they will try to answer is: What is the moon made of? This could prove difficult to do on the spot, even if the explorers have geological training. The rock and other material may be completely foreign. (Some scientists have theorized that the moon antedates the earth and may have been created by a different cosmological process.) This is why they have planned to take 50 pounds of samples back with them for laboratory analysis, along with many photographs and on-the-spot maps. One thing they will be alert for is signs of water, perhaps ice in a cavern, and any evidence of life.

In the dim past, it is possible the moon did have an atmosphere which eventually leaked away because of the planet's low gravity, one-sixth that of earth's. It might have kept alive some primitive life forms for a while, perhaps single-celled plants and animals picked up in a close brush with earth.

There may be some real surprises, although many

Drawing of an Apollo-Saturn V heading into space from Cape Kennedy "Moonport," Complex 39.
—NASA photograph

scientists doubt it after looking at Ranger's lunar closeup pictures. Dr. Harold C. Urey, a Nobel prize-winning chemist, has said the explorers probably would discover only "a rather dull cinder."

But the physical dangers will make the trip itself anything but dull. All the way out and back the astronauts will have to worry about meteoroids flashing across their path and the possibility of a sudden solar flare bathing them in deadly radiation. A meteoroid the size of a walnut moving at 100,000 miles per hour could tear into their spacecraft and kill them all with the shock wave. If it is any comfort, scientists say their studies have shown few meteoroids that big; most are like grains of sand and easily repelled by the aluminum honeycomb skin of the spacecraft. Other scientists say solar flares are predictable by several days and the spacecraft offers sufficient protection against all but the worst.

The most hazardous part of the trip will be getting back. First, the explorers will have to make a virtually unassisted takeoff from the moon. Their 3,000-pound-thrust ascent engine gives them just one chance to accelerate into orbit at 3,600 miles per hour. If it quits, they will drop back on the moon and perish. Next comes the crucial rendezvous and linkup with the orbiting mother ship. If the "Bug's" controls fail at this point, there will still be an opportunity for the astronaut left in the mother ship to maneuver alongside and rescue them.

The truly hair-raising moment of all will come 60 hours later, after the Apollo has rocketed out of lunar orbit, leaving the "Bug" behind, and is approaching earth. Pulled by the earth's gravity, the spaceship will be traveling again at 25,-000 miles per hour. In order to re-enter safely, the astronauts will have to jettison their service module and hit a "corridor" only 40 miles deep in the earth's upper atmosphere. If they come in too steeply, they will be crushed by unbearable gravity forces; too shallowly, they will spin out into a long orbit about the earth that will be equally fatal.

The flight plan calls for two penetrations of the atmosphere to dissipate the command module's tremendous speed. It will plunge first to within 200,000 feet of land, then skip to 400,000 feet, and finally, after sailing halfway about the globe, come blazing down over the Pacific Ocean near the island of Pago Pago.

In the final minutes the astronauts will have to depend upon Apollo's three big balloon parachutes

to lower them gently to the water — and rescue by Navy ships and helicopters.

Should the great adventure actually come about in this fashion, new insight will be gained into the moon's origin and nature. And the human spirit will be raised immeasurably by such an exploit of dedication and courage.

For Americans it is bound to be the most wildly exciting week in history — no matter if the Russians have landed first — and perhaps the fulfillment of a dream passed down from Lucian of Samosata.

CIVILIAN MANNED SPACECRAFT

Gemini IV launch, Cape Kennedy, June 3, 1965.
—NASA photograph

GEMINI A (U.S.)

Type: Manned orbital spacecraft.

Contracting agency or military service: National Aeronautics and Space Administration.

Mission: Gather space flight experience in preparation for Apollo moon program (flights up to two weeks).

Status: Operational.

Capacity: Two men.

Performance: Range — global. Apogee — varying up to about 300 miles. Speed — 18,000 m.p.h. Special characteristics — maneuverable and capable of rendezvous with other spacecraft. Re-entry — controlled ballistic. Landing — by parachute on water.

Specifications: Configuration — bell-shaped. Length — 18.75 ft. (over-all). Diameter — 10 ft. (at base). Weight — about 7,000 lbs. Re-entry module — 11 ft. in length; 7.5 ft. in diameter (at base). Guidance — inertial (pilot controlled). Spacecraft propulsion — hypergolic thrusters (nitrogen and hydrazine). Cabin environment — 100 per cent oxygen at 5 psi. Spacecraft power — batteries and fuel cells. Booster — Titan II.

Principal contractors: Prime — McDonnell. Frame — McDonnell. Life support system — Garrett. Guidance — IBM/Minneapolis-Honeywell. Propulsion — NAA. Communications — Collins. Fuel cells — GE. Spacesuit — Clark.

History: Gemini was started in late 1961 as a follow-on program to Mercury, the first U.S. manned spacecraft. Twelve Gemini capsules were built. Manned flights began with the third launching, March 23, 1965. Design of the spacecraft and spacesuit permitted limited activities by astronauts outside the spacecraft while in orbit. Flights scheduled through 1967. The Mercury program was started in 1958. Two manned suborbital flights were conducted in 1961. Four orbital flights — the longest 34 hours — were conducted in 1962 and 1963. Estimated cost of Mercury: 400 million dollars. Estimated cost of Gemini: 1.3 billion dollars (see Military Spacecraft for Air Force Gemini B). In 1965 an astronaut walked outside of orbiting Gemini IV, Gemini V orbited for 8 days, taking the lead for the U.S. from Russia. Fuel cell power system proved operational for the first time on Gemini V, as well as on-board radar.

Gemini Tracking Network

Almost continual contact can be maintained with Gemini capsules while in orbit by the following global network of 14 stations:

Kano, Nigeria	Point Arguello, California
One range ship in the Indian Ocean	Guaymas, Mexico
Zanzibar	Corpus Christi, Texas
Muchea, Australia	Cape Kennedy, Florida
Woomera, Australia	One range ship in the Atlantic Ocean
Canton Island	Bermuda
Kauai, Hawaii	Canary Islands

Apollo spacecraft being mated to Saturn launch vehicle.
—NASA photograph

APOLLO (U.S.)

Type: Manned lunar spacecraft.

Contracting agency or military service: National Aeronautics and Space Administration.

Mission: Manned lunar expedition.

Status: Flight testing.

Capacity: Three men.

Performance: Range — approximately 500,000 miles. Speed — 25,000 m.p.h. Special characteristics — maneuverable in earth orbit, cislunar travel and lunar orbit. Carries two-man lunar excursion module (LEM). Designed for orbital rendezvous and docking. Re-entry — controlled ballistic. Landing — by parachute on water.

Specifications: Configuration — conical. Length — 45 ft. (over-all). Diameter — 13 ft. Weight — nearly 90,000 lbs. (over-all). Command module — 12 ft. high, 13 ft. in diameter at base, internal volume 300 cu. ft., weight about 10,000 lbs. Service module — 20 ft. in length, 13 ft. in diameter, weight about

50,000 lbs. (loaded). LEM — 12 ft. in length (with landing gear folded), 8 ft. in diameter, weight approximately 30,000 lbs. Spacecraft propulsion — hypergolic thrusters for maneuvering and 22,000-lb.-thrust rocket in service module; 10,500-lb.-thrust descent rocket and 3,000-lb. ascent rocket for LEM. Life support capability — two weeks (command module), two days (LEM). Cabin environment — 100 per cent oxygen at 5 psi. Spacecraft power — fuel cells. Booster — Saturn I-B (earth-orbital test flights); Saturn V (lunar missions).

Principal contractors: Spacecraft prime — NAA. LEM — Grumman. System integration and checkout — GE. Guidance and navigation — MIT and AC Sparkplug. Attitude control — Minneapolis-Honeywell. Communications—Collins. Fuel cells—United Aircraft. Environmental control — Garrett. Heat shield — Avco. Service module propulsion — Aerojet. LEM propulsion — TRW (descent), Bell (ascent). Environmental system (LEM) and lunar spacesuits — United Aircraft.

History: Initiated by President Kennedy in May 1961 in response to Soviet challenge in space. Initial objective: to land Americans on the moon before the end of the 1960's. Program called for major mobilization of United States industry including some 300,000 people. Estimated cost: 20–40 billion dollars. First unmanned orbital flights began in 1964. Manned flights scheduled beginning in 1967.

Apollo Deep Space Tracking Network

Goldstone, California
Johannesburg, South Africa
Woomera, Australia
Mobile units aboard ships

SPACE BOOSTERS (CIVILIAN)

SATURN (U.S.)

Type: Class of three heavy launch vehicles.

Contracting agency: National Aeronautics and Space Administration.

Status: Development and testing.

Mission: Orbital manned space flight and lunar exploration.

Performance: Saturn I — boost 10 tons into low earth orbit or 5,000 lbs. to moon. Saturn I-B — boost 16 tons into low earth orbit or 8,000 lbs. to moon. Saturn V — boost 120 tons into low earth orbit or 45 tons to moon.

Specifications: Saturn I — 2 stages, 120 ft. over-all length, 22 ft. in diameter at base. First stage propulsion — 8 LOX-kerosene-fueled H-1 engines delivering total of 1.5 million lbs. thrust. Second stage — 6 LOX-liquid-hydrogen-fueled RL-10 engines delivering total of 90,000 lbs. thrust. Saturn I-B — 2 stages, 142 ft. over-all length, 22 ft. in diameter at base. First stage propulsion — 8 LOX-kerosene-fueled H-1 engines delivering a total of 1.6 million lbs. thrust. Second stage — 1 LOX-

Saturn I carrying Apollo "boilerplate" model.
—NASA photograph

liquid-hydrogen-fueled J-2 engine delivering 200,-000 lbs. thrust. Saturn V — 3 stages, 280 ft. over-all length, 33 ft. in diameter at base. First stage propulsion — 5 LOX-kerosene-fueled F-1 engines delivering a total of 7.5 million lbs. thrust. Second stage — 5 LOX-liquid-hydrogen-fueled J-2 engines delivering a total of 1 million lbs. thrust. Third stage — one 200,000-lb.-thrust J-2 engine.

Principal contractors: R&D prime — NASA's Marshall Space Flight Center, Huntsville, Ala. Production primes — Chrysler (Saturn I and I-B first stages), Boeing (Saturn V first stages), Douglas (Saturn I-B second stage and Saturn V third stage), NAA (Saturn V second stage). Engine primes — NAA (H-1, F-1 and J-2), United Aircraft (RL-10).

History: R&D was begun in 1958 as a Defense Department project under the then Army Ballistic Missile Agency, Huntsville, Ala. The Eisenhower Administration ruled there was no military requirement for a large space booster and transferred it to NASA. The transfer included the project director, Dr. Wernher von Braun. Development of the Saturn I-B and V versions began in 1961 after initiation of the Apollo lunar program. Production models are being built at Michaud, La., in a huge NASA plant. Proof-testing in captive ground firings is conducted at NASA's Mississippi Test Facility, 30 miles from New Orleans. Ten Saturn I's were built and launched 1961-1965; 12 Saturn I-B's were to be built and launched 1966-1968, 8 with men aboard; 15 Saturn V's were to be built and launched 1967-1970, 8 to 10 with men aboard. Saturn I's were used only to orbit Pegasus meteor-oid-detection satellites and "boilerplate" Apollos. Saturn I-B's were intended to orbit partially fueled Apollos in "everything up" tests. Saturn V's were designed to practice the full lunar mission in earth orbit before the big jump off about 1970. NASA also planned to use the huge rocket for orbiting space stations and advanced probes of Mars and other planets. The addition of a nuclear-fueled stage, NERVA (being developed under Project Rover), was under consideration.

TITAN II (U.S.)

Type: Medium-weight launch vehicle.

Contracting agency: Air Force.

Status: Operational.

Mission: Gemini launch vehicle.

Performance: Payload — more than 7,000 lbs. into earth orbit for prolonged missions. Total thrust — 530,-000 lbs. (first stage — 430,000 lbs.; second stage — 100,000 lbs.)

Specifications: Two-stage rocket, 90 ft. tall. First stage — 71 ft. Second stage — 19 ft. Diameter both stages — 10 ft. Total weight (fueled) — 165 tons. Propulsion — two 215,000-lb.-thrust engines using storable liquid propellants (hydrazine and unsym-metrical dimethylhydrozine [UDMH] with nitrogen tetroxide as oxidizer) in first stage; one 100,000-lb.-thrust engine using same propellants in second stage. Propellants are hypergolic (burn on contact). No ignition system needed. Guidance — radio.

Principal contractors: Prime — Martin. Propulsion — Aerojet. Guidance — GE with Burroughs computer.

History: Developed from Titan II ICBM.

Titan II in action with Gemini spacecraft, 1965.
—NASA photograph

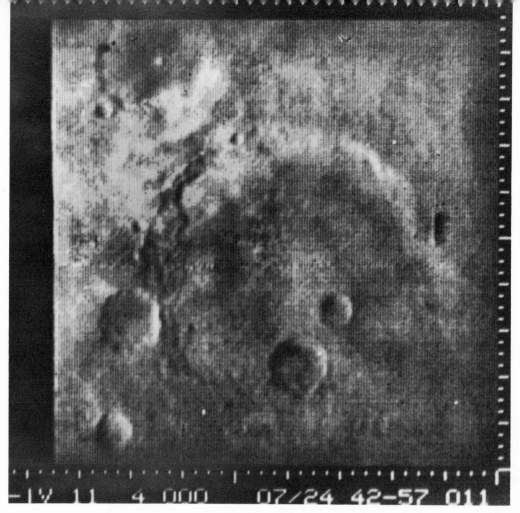

−IV 11 4 000 07/24 42-57 011

Top, historic picture of Mars, snapped July 14, 1965
by Mariner IV from 7,800 miles reveals a surface much
like the moon's, seen below in closeup by Ranger IX
from 775 miles.

—NASA photographs

2

SPACE EXPLORATION: SCIENTISTS AMONG THE SPHERES

Life began on earth under a warm, vaporous blanket called the atmosphere as if encased in a celestial womb. It is within that womb that mankind has existed for some 250,000 years and looked out at all the wonders and mysteries of the universe.

It has fallen to us, in this age, to pierce the protective envelope and explore the unknown that lies in apparently endless space.

Scientists — and the objectives of scientists — are the prime movers of this exploration. Practical applications of what they may discover will come later — although improved weather forecasting, radio communications and navigational aids are already with us.

This major search for fundamental knowledge began in the mid-1950's and has been conducted to a greater or lesser degree by more than forty nations around the world. The United States and the Soviet Union are the leaders. And, of the two, the United States has been by far the more active.

Instrument-carrying United States satellites are probing the total environment of space, sun-earth relationships, geodetic properties of the earth, physical properties of the earth's moon, properties of other planets, the over-all fundamental nature of the universe, and the nature of possible extra-terrestrial life.

Space is a frigid, almost absolute vacuum. But it has physical properties that must be understood to pursue manned space flight. These properties also govern the use of satellites for practical applications and their design.

Study of the physical relations between the sun and earth is important because the sun is the major source of the earth's energy. Among other effects, the sun's energy has a direct bearing on weather, long-range climatic conditions and communications.

Obtaining new knowledge of the earth's geodetic properties — its shape and orbital eccentricities — means better maps and more accurate launching of space vehicles as well as military missiles. In fact, this kind of information, which is vital to accurate performance of ICBM's, was one of the first major benefits the Russians received from their so-called "peaceful" Sputniks at the dawn of the Space Age.

New knowledge of the moon's physical properties not only aids all lunar landing programs but also contributes to basic knowledge of the origin of the earth. A major question that scientists wish to resolve is whether the moon and the earth were formed at the same time or whether the moon is an older body that was captured by the earth. New knowledge of the properties of planets other than the earth also could help explain the origin of the

15

earth itself as well as the solar system.

The most scientifically important project is the gathering of new information about the fundamental nature of the universe and the possibility of extraterrestrial life. Scientists feel that these two areas have greatest and most exciting potential for yielding basic knowledge which could result in significant and possibly revolutionary scientific concepts.

A typical example of the kind of new knowledge coming out of the United States space program is the discovery that space is not a huge void separating the planets and stars. Instruments carried by satellites and unmanned spacecraft have shown that space is filled with molecules of gas and bits of cosmic dust. Moreover, it is alive with charged particles — protons, beta rays, alpha rays, gamma rays, X rays and occasional cosmic rays.

Readings taken by space probes and satellites show that some of the radiation pouring from the sun is a plasma of charged gas moving in a constant stream. This is the so-called "solar wind," which is subject to magnetic forces that "blow" it into different patterns. A Mariner spacecraft en route to Venus in 1962 discovered the solar wind is more like a blast from a jet nozzle. The molecules of charged gas had a temperature of 1 million degrees Fahrenheit and a velocity ranging from 720,000 to 1.8 million miles per hour.

Still more new data have enabled scientists to compute the age of our solar system. It is estimated to be about 6 billion years old.

Significant space programs are under way in the United Kingdom, Canada, France, West Germany, Italy and Japan. And the nations of Western Europe have banded together in a number of joint scientific space programs.

NASA is helping a dozen nations in the launching of sounding rockets abroad. At the same time, many nations are launching sounding rockets from United States ranges. Several countries also are placing experiments aboard United States scientific satellites.

By 1965, the entire world had launched into orbit well over 300 spacecraft and satellites of all types, both military and civilian. Of these, nearly 250 were American; one was Italian; one Canadian; one a joint U.S.-British satellite; the rest were Russian.

Satellites and unmanned spacecraft wresting secrets from space vary from sounding rockets not much larger than large skyrockets to multiarmed vehicles festooned with dozens of sensors. An almost equally varied number of launch vehicles have been designed to boost these payloads into orbit or inject them into lunar and planetary trajectories. The rockets range from the slim, relatively small 72-foot Scout to the mighty Saturns.

The cost of launching satellites and spacecraft has remained high. The approximate cost of a Scout including launching expenses was estimated by NASA in the mid-1960's to be about 1 million dollars. It can put 240 pounds into low orbit. NASA's estimated cost for an Atlas-Agena approached 8 million dollars. It can loft 500 pounds to the moon.

Total United States expenditure on scientific space programs has continued to be only a minor part of the space budget. The total annual expenditure for all United States space sciences and space applications programs during the mid-1960's has averaged about three-quarters of a billion dollars.

A sizeable portion of the money has been spent on applied space science — the fields of communications and meteorology. This activity has offered the earliest chance of a direct payoff from all the billions being expended on all space programs.

Less than a decade after Sputnik I shocked the West into moving into space, the U.S. Weather Bureau was using data from the Tiros meteorological satellites in forecasting the weather; millions of Americans watched part of the funeral of Sir Winston Churchill on television via the Telstar communications satellite; Polaris submarines used the Transit navigational satellite to check their positions at sea; and the first Early Bird commercial communications satellite was placed in orbit by a private corporation.

While scientists moved steadily toward the receding stars, near space had become a spot almost not too far from home. And the major policy question that has begun to be debated by leading scientists is what major programs the United States should undertake after the first men land on the moon.

One school of thought advocates building moon bases; another, large space stations; a third, the exploration of Mars.

For some scientists Mars holds the greatest appeal. It is the only planet in our solar system which may harbor some form of life — plants, if anything. Exobiologists — those who think life is not unique to the earth — long have favored sending instrumented probes to land on Mars and radio back whether there is something growing there. This would be the aim of NASA's Voyager spacecraft, planned for a shot in 1971.

But the exobiologists have run into difficulty trying to figure out what type of instruments to send, since Martian life, if it exists, could be radically different from earth life. What should the instruments look for? The scientists have been disturbed at the thought of a spacecraft landing on Mars and contaminating it with germs and microscopic spores of earth life. This would destroy the whole experiment. But sterilizing spacecraft, especially when done with heat, can ruin electronic equipment, thus presenting still another barrier.

The historic flight of Mariner IV past Mars on July 14, 1965 greatly diminished the hopes of finding life or evidence that life once existed there as we know it on earth. The Mariner spacecraft transmitted 21 photographs back to earth. All were taken between 10,500 and 6,300 miles above the unpromising Martian surface. And all told the same story of a bleak, cratered surface very much like the surface of the earth's moon.

No trace of the famous "canals" was found. There was no sign of erosion; no sign of habitation; no sign of bodies of water. Radio signals from Mariner showed that the Martian atmosphere through which they passed was about 4 to 7 millibars — comparable to the atmosphere 100,000 feet above the earth and but a gasp away from the vacuum of space. However, the presence of some form of life in the dark areas that spread and shrink on the Martian surface with the seasons was not precluded.

Sending men to Mars would cost anywhere up to 100 billion dollars — no one is certain of the exact figure. It is impossible for the United States to try it before the 1980's. Neither a propulsion system — nuclear or nuclear-electric — nor the spaceships that could sustain men for more than a year of flight could be perfected until then. Moreover, after 1971, Mars' orbit puts it into an unfavorable position relative to the earth, keeping the two planets separated by more than 100 million miles. In the 1980's, it will once again come fairly close — 35 million miles — at two-year intervals.

Landing an expedition on Mars would be more hazardous than on the moon. The planet's gravity is almost the same as earth's and its atmosphere is about as thin as that on the top of Mt. Everest.

This is enough to cause severe heating of an entering spacecraft, but not enough to support a parachute to assist in a gentle landing. There are many other major dangers and obstacles.

It is doubtful that scientific curiosity alone will spur the United States to undertake such a costly and difficult exploration. Some other compelling reason must arise before Americans try to walk on Mars.

SCIENTIFIC SATELLITES

Ranger 8 launched by Atlas-Agena B vehicles, 1965.
—NASA photograph

RANGER (U.S.)

Type: Instrumented lunar exploration vehicle.
Contracting agency: Jet Propulsion Laboratory (NASA).
Status: Operational.
Mission: "Hard" impact on the moon.
Performance: Range — about 240,000 miles. Launch — on top of Atlas-Agena B. Lunar landing — capsule slowed by retrorocket probably will hit moon at about 150 m.p.h.
Specifications: Height — 11 ft. Diameter at base — 5

ft. Span of solar panels extended in flight — 15 ft. Total weight — 800 lbs.

Instrumentation: Vehicle — gamma ray spectrometer to measure lunar surface radiation, vidicon telescope.

Principal contractor: Prime — Aeronutronic.

History: Conceived in 1959, Ranger was the first of a series of instrumented probes to precede manned United States flight to the moon. In operation, the vidicon telescope was designed to be activated at about 2,000 miles altitude above the moon. The first five Ranger spacecraft failed in missions. Ranger 6 impacted on the moon close to target area, but cameras failed. Ranger 7 returned 4,713 high-quality photographs before impacting. Rangers 8 and 9 each took more than 7,000 pictures when launched in early 1965 and completed the program.

Surveyor.

—NASA photograph

SURVEYOR (U.S.)

Type: Instrumented lunar spacecraft.

Contracting agency: Jet Propulsion Laboratory (NASA).

Status: R&D.

Mission: Soft-land instruments on the moon to obtain data for design of manned spacecraft.

Performance: Range — 240,000 miles. Launch — on top of Atlas-Centaur. Lunar landing — cushioned by retrorockets and mechanically.

Specifications: Height — about 8 ft. Weight — 2,150 lbs.

Instrumentation: Scientific payload of 65 lbs. will contain color television cameras and a drill to pick up a sample of the lunar crust which will be analyzed in a chromatograph and spectrometers. The TV camera images of the moon's features and other information picked up by the various instruments will be transmitted back to earth.

Principal contractor: Hughes.

History: Conceived in 1960, Surveyor's design was undertaken in 1961. Launching of the first of these spacecraft toward various parts of the moon slipped from 1963 to 1965. Capable only of one-position observation, Surveyor nevertheless will provide United States scientists with their first look at the moon from the lunar surface itself. The analysis of the lunar crust is intended to determine whether there are present any organic molecules that might constitute primordial life forms. Chemical and mineral consistency will be recorded along with radiation intensity, magnetism, surface temperatures, and the lunar atmosphere — knowledge imperative for man's survival on the moon. A second series of 2,500-lb. Surveyors is also planned.

Pegasus in orbit (artist's concept).

—NASA photograph

PEGASUS (U.S.)

Type: Unmanned scientific satellite.

Contracting agency: National Aeronautics and Space Administration.

Status: Operational.

Mission: Meteoroid detection.

Performance: Range — 300- to 800-mile orbit. Launch — on top of Saturn I. Instrumentation — two detection wings that will be extended in orbit.

Specifications: Weight — 3,400 lbs. Wings — 50 ft. long, 15 ft. wide.

Principal contractor: Prime — Fairchild Hiller.

History: First successful launching in 1965. Two more launchings scheduled. Cislunar Pegasus planned for 1968.

Lunar Orbiter model.

LUNAR ORBITER (U.S.)

Type: Lunar reconnaissance satellite.

Contracting agency: Langley Research Center (NASA).

Status: R&D.

Mission: Photograph lunar surface to select landing sites for manned spacecraft.

Performance: Range — about 240,000 miles. Lunar orbit — about 575 miles (circular); perilunar orbit with low point of about 28 miles from lunar surface. Launch — on top of Atlas-Agena. On-board propulsion — 100-lb.-thrust bipropellant rocket engine. Power source — solar cells (266 watts). Life — six months to one year; camera system operational about one month.

Specifications: Height — 5.5 ft. Diameter — 5 ft. Total weight — about 800 lbs. Carries 4 solar panels, each 12 ft. square, arranged in cloverleaf.

Instrumentation: Camera system capable of resolution of one meter over 3,000-square-mile area; sun and star sensors for pitch, yaw and roll reference.

Principal contractors: Prime — Boeing. Power and com-

munication — RCA. Camera system — Eastman Kodak.

History: Program started in 1963. First of five flights scheduled to begin in 1966.

Mariner IV Mars explorer.

MARINER (U.S.)

Type: Instrumented interplanetary probe.

Contracting agency: Jet Propulsion Laboratory (NASA).

Status: R&D.

Mission: Fly close to Mars and Venus to obtain rudimentary data on the two planets nearest to earth.

Performance: Range — 25 million-plus miles (will probably go into orbit around the sun). Launch — on top of Atlas-Agena B or Atlas-Centaur.

Specifications: Height — about 5 ft. Weight — 575 lbs. Frame — somewhat similar to Ranger.

Instrumentation: Spacecraft payload includes a radiometer to scan the surface of cloud-shrouded Venus for temperature distribution, an ultraviolet spectrometer to examine the planet's atmosphere, and a magnetometer to study the magnetic field.

Principal contractor: JPL.

History: Conceived in 1960, Mariner failed in its first attempt at a Venus fly-by in August 1962. The second passed within 21,000 miles of Venus in December 1962. The fourth Mariner was successfully launched toward Mars on November 28, 1964, on a 7-month flight to the red planet. It flew past Mars July 14, 1965, taking 21 pictures from 10,500 to 6,300 miles above the cratered Martian surface and transmitting them to earth. Plans for 1966 and 1969 Mariner launchings to Mars were canceled.

Voyager concept.

—NASA photograph

VOYAGER (U.S.)

Type: Instrumented planetary exploratory spacecraft.

Contracting Agency: Jet Propulsion Laboratory (NASA).

Status: Study.

Mission: Orbit Venus and Mars (in several separate flights) and drop instrumented capsules for ground exploration — specifically, to determine whether life exists on these planets, and in what form.

Performance: Range — 25 million-plus miles. Launch — on top of Saturn. Planetary landing — parachute and retrorockets.

Specifications: Height — undetermined. Total weight of vehicle — about 2,400 lbs. Propulsion — will carry retrorockets for injection into orbit around a planet.

Instrumentation: Capsule equipment includes television camera and geophysical measuring devices. Spacecraft will drop capsules on planets and relay to earth data radioed from instruments in capsules.

Principal contractor: Avco, GE, Lockheed.

History: Conceived in 1960, Voyager is designed to be placed in orbit around Venus and Mars in 1971-1973. It will be the forerunner of manned interplanetary space travel.

TIROS (U.S.)

Type: First-generation weather satellite.

Contracting agency: National Aeronautics and Space Administration, U.S. Weather Bureau.

Status: Operational.

Mission: Prove feasibility of global weather forecasting system; interim operational system.

Performance: Orbit — 370 to 460 miles. Launched by Thor-Delta.

Specifications: Height — 22 in. Diameter — 42 in. Weight — about 300 lbs. Power supply — solar cells and storage batteries.

Instrumentation: Narrow- and wide-angle TV cameras, radiation scanners.

Principal contractors: Prime — RCA. Frame — RCA. Instrumentation — RCA.

History: The first Tiros was launched in April 1960 and performed very satisfactorily. In subsequent shots, some difficulties occurred with the TV cameras. Nevertheless, Tiros proved the system was feasible and Tiros in a new cartwheel configuration (TOS) was converted into an interim national operational system.

NIMBUS (U.S.)

Type: Second-generation weather satellite.

Contracting agency: National Aeronautics and Space Administration.

Status: Flight testing.

Mission: World-wide 24-hour weather surveillance.

Performance: Orbit — 600 miles, quasi-polar. Launched on top of Thor-Agena B.

Specifications: Height — 118 in. Weight — 830 lbs. Power supply — solar cells mounted in paddle wheels.

Instrumentation: Vidicon cameras for recording cloud movements, radiation sensors, radar.

Principal contractors: Prime — NASA. Integration, stabilization system, testing — GE.

History: R&D was started in 1960 on Nimbus as the operational version of the experimental Tiros. Nimbus I, successfully launched in 1964, transmitted more than 27,000 pictures. Nimbus II was scheduled for 1966.

Orbiting Astronomical Observatory (OAO).

—NASA photograph

OAO (U.S.)

Type: Orbiting astronomical observatory.

Contracting agency: National Aeronautics and Space Administration.

Status: R&D.

Mission: Telescopic observation of the stars and the universe.

Performance: Orbit — 500 miles, circular. Launched on Atlas-Agena B.

Specifications: Length — 116 in. Diameter — 80 in. Weight — 3,300 lbs. (including 1,000 lbs. of instruments). Power supply — solar cells and batteries (about 1,000 watts).

Instrumentation: Television tube, telemetry, spectrometer, and 24-in. mirror for telescope.

Principal contractors: Prime — Grumman. Components — Westinghouse. Stabilization and control — GE.

History: OAO will give man his first opportunity to view the stars outside of the atmosphere, expected to revolutionize astronomy. First launchings are scheduled for 1965-1966.

OGO (U.S.)

Type: Orbiting geophysical measurement observatory.

Contracting agency: National Aeronautics and Space Administration.

Status: R&D.

Mission: Take measurements of earth.

Performance: Orbit — 140 to 500 miles in polar orbit (POGO) and 150 to 92,000 miles in eccentric orbit (EGO). Launched on Atlas-Agena B, Thor-Agena B, or Centaur. Orbital life — 1 year.

Specifications: Height — 68 in. Weight — 1,070 lbs. Power supply — solar cells and batteries (560 watts).

Instrumentation: Can carry 50 different experiments and transmitting equipment.

Principal contractor: Prime — STL.

History: The first OGO, launched in 1964, was partly successful. The second of a half-dozen planned launches is scheduled for 1965.

OSO (U.S.)

Type: Orbiting solar observatory.

Contracting agency: National Aeronautics and Space Administration.

Status: R&D.

Mission: Take radiation measurements of the sun.

Performance: Orbit — circular, 300 miles. Launched on Thor-Delta.

Specifications: Height — 37 in. Weight — 440-490 lbs. Power supply — solar cells (28 watts).

Instrumentation: Spectrometers to measure ultraviolet radiation and X rays; equipment for monitoring gamma rays.

Principal contractor: Prime — Ball Brothers.

History: OSO 1 was launched successfully in 1961. A total of eight OSO's is planned through 1968. A follow-on program is also planned.

Early Bird.

EARLY BIRD (U.S.)

Type: Communications satellite (synchronous).

Contracting agency: ComSat Corp.

Status: Flight testing.

Mission: To provide data leading to an operational commercial communications satellite system.

Performance: Range — 22,300-mile synchronous orbit. Launch — on top of TAD (Thrust Augmented Delta). Traffic capability — 240 two-way telephone channels between the United States and Europe.

Specifications: Height — 23.25 in. Diameter — 28.4 in. Weight — 85 lbs.

Principal contractors: Prime — Hughes. Launch services — NASA.

History: First Early Bird successfully placed in orbit in 1965. A full global system was scheduled for 1967.

ECHO (U.S.)

Type: Experimental passive communications satellite.

Contracting agency: National Aeronautics and Space Administration.

Status: Flight testing.

Mission: Prove feasibility of reflecting radio signals off surface of 135-ft. sphere.

Performance: Launched in 1962 into a 700- to 800-mile circular polar orbit. Launched on top of Thor-Agena B.

Instrumentation: Tracking beacons on the sphere, also solar cells and batteries.

Principal contractors: Prime — NASA. Sphere (mylar

plastic and aluminum foil laminate) — G. T. Schjeldahl Co.

History: Echo I was placed in orbit in August 1960, Echo II in January 1964.

GEOS (U.S.)

Type: Geodetic explorer.

Contracting agency: NASA.

Status: Operational.

Mission: Produce accurate maps of the world.

Performance: Orbit — 700 to 1,300 miles. Launch — TAD.

Specifications: Weight — 385 lbs. Carries 322 prisms to reflect laser beams from earth. Stabilized by 60-foot extension boom called a gravity gradient.

Instrumentation: Flashing light beacons, radio beacons, laser and radar reflectors.

Principal contractors: Prime — APL. Gravity gradient — GE.

History: Geos I was launched Nov. 6, 1965 and began producing data for highly detailed maps of the earth. The information also was being employed to pinpoint targets for U.S. ICBM's and pick out guide-posts for Apollo astronauts. Satellite has a military counterpart, ANNA, built by the U.S. Army.

TELSTAR (U.S.)

Type: Communications satellite (low altitude, active).

Contracting agency: American Telephone & Telegraph Co.

Status: Operational flight testing.

Mission: Test broadband microwave communications satellite system.

Performance: Range — 3,500- to 580-mile orbit (Telstar I); 6,700- to 600-mile orbit (Telstar II). Launch — on top of Thor-Delta.

Specifications: Height — 34 in. Diameter — 34 in. Weight — 175 lbs.

Principal contractor: Prime — AT&T.

History: First commercial communications satellite. Launched by NASA for AT&T on a reimbursed basis. Telstar I was successfully placed in orbit on July 10, 1962, Telstar II on May 7, 1963. Telstars provided first TV transmission between the United States and Europe. NASA developed a very similar satellite, Relay, and successfully launched two of them in 1962-1963.

Telstar II.

—NASA photograph

Advanced Technological Satellite (ATS).

—Hughes Aircraft Co. photograph

ADVANCED TECHNOLOGICAL SATELLITE (U.S.)

Type: Unmanned scientific satellite.

Contracting agency: Goddard Space Flight Center (NASA).

Status: R&D.

Mission: Test bed for advanced satellite components, particularly for communications and meteorological satellites.

Performance: Range — 6,500-mile and synchronous orbits. Launch — on top of Atlas-Agena D.

Specifications: Length — 52 to 78 in., depending on model. Diameter — 58 in. Weight — 800 lbs.

Instrumentation: High- and low-resolution cameras, communications equipment, gravity gradient stabilization systems.

Principal contractors: Prime — Hughes. Gravity gradient systems — GE.

History: Advanced Technological Satellite (ATS) is an outgrowth of the Syncom communications satellite program. Five flights over a period of several years are scheduled to begin in late 1966-early 1967.

BIOS satellite to orbit primates.
—General Electric Co. photograph

BIOS (U.S.)

Type: Biological laboratory satellite.

Contracting agency: Ames Research Center (NASA).

Status: R&D.

Mission: Test effects of space up to 30 days on living organisms.

Performance: Range — 200-mile circular orbit. Launch — on top of Delta and TAD space vehicles. Reentry capsule — ejected by satellite and recovered from ocean. Payload — plants, beetles, monkeys. Power source — batteries and fuel cells for various flights.

Specifications: Length — 93 in. Diameter — 44 in. Weight — 875 to 1,250 lbs. depending on mission length.

Instrumentation: Data recording, time-lapse photography, life support system.

Principal contractors: Prime — GE. Fuel cells — GE.

History: Program started in 1963. First of six flights were scheduled to begin in 1966.

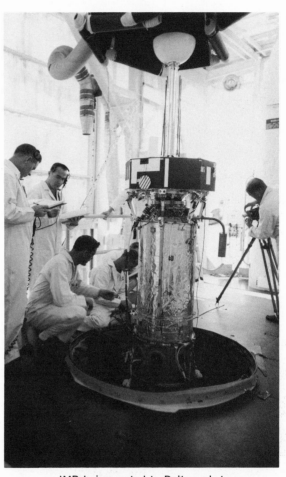

IMP being mated to Delta rocket.
—NASA photograph

IMP (U.S.)

Type: Unmanned scientific satellite.

Contracting agency: National Aeronautics and Space Administration.

Status: Operational.

Mission: Measurement of magnetic fields and particles between the earth and the moon.

Performance: Range — orbital apogee of 100,000 miles. Launch — on top of Delta and TAD.

Specifications: Weight — about 135 lbs.

Principal contractor: Prime — Goddard Space Flight Center (NASA).

History: IMP (Interplanetary Monitoring Platform) was first launched successfully in 1963. IMP II was successfully launched in 1964. A total of seven flights have been scheduled.

Britain's UK-C, 1964.

—NASA photograph

UK-3 (UNITED KINGDOM)

Type: Unmanned scientific satellite.

Contracting agency: British universities.

Status: R&D.

Mission: Study various space phenomena including radio propagation, noise, and molecular oxygen.

Specifications: Weight — 132 lbs. Launch — on top of Scout.

Principal contractor: Prime — Royal Aircraft Establishment.

History: Scheduled to be launched in 1967. Forerunners of the UK-3 were the 1964 UK-C and the 1961 S-51. Both investigated ionospheric phenomena and were launched by the United States.

ISIS (CANADA)

Type: Unmanned scientific satellite.

Contracting agency: Defense Research Telecommunications Laboratory (DRTL).

Status: R&D.

Mission: Ionospheric studies that follow earlier studies by Canada's Alouette (Topside Sounder) satellite.

Specifications: Weight — 350 lbs.

Principal contractor: Prime — DRTL.

History: Three launchings scheduled by NASA for Canada beginning in 1967.

D-2 (FRANCE)

Type: Unmanned scientific satellite.

Contracting agency: Centre National d'Etudes Spatiales (CNES).

Status: R&D.

Mission: Study atomic hydrogen in the exosphere.

Early San Marco test.

—NASA photograph

SAN MARCO (ITALY)

Type: Unmanned scientific satellite.

Contracting agency: Italian Space Commission/University of Rome.

Status: Operational.

Mission: To make ionospheric studies and measure aerodynamic drag.

Performance: Range — about a 250-mile orbit. Launch — on top of Scout.

Specifications: Weight — 210 lbs.

Principal contractor: Prime — Italian Space Commission.

History: Successfully launched in 1964.

Specifications: Weight — 176 lbs. Launch — on top of Diamant.

Principal contractor: Prime — CNES.

History: Scheduled to be launched in 1968. A D-3 satellite scheduled for launching in the same period is designed to make global meteorological studies.

MOLNIYA 1 (U.S.S.R.)

Type: Experimental communications satellite.

Contracting agency: Not disclosed.

Status: Operational.

Mission: Relay TV and voice transmissions.

Performance: Orbit — 298 to 23,628 miles. Launch vehicle — not disclosed.

Specifications: Weight — not disclosed. Active repeater transmission with about 500-channel capacity. Powered by solar cells and rechargeable batteries. Contains spacecraft orientation system.

History: Launched April 23, 1965. First announced Soviet comsat. Name means "Lightning." Its arrival was three years after first United States comsat, Telstar.

PROTON (U.S.S.R.)

Type: Scientific space station.

Contracting agency: Soviet Academy of Sciences.

Status: Operational.

Mission: Study solar proton and cosmic radiations.

Performance: In 114- to 376-mile orbit.

Specifications: Weight — 27,000 lbs. Dimensions — not disclosed. Power supply — solar-cell panels and batteries.

Instrumentation: Ionization calorimeter and other equipment to measure cosmic particles and their interaction with matter.

History: Two launched by new Soviet space booster in 1965 — the heaviest objects placed in orbit until then. Soviet scientists described the satellite as a type of cosmic atom-smasher that might provide new insight into the nature of matter.

ELEKTRON (U.S.S.R.)

Type: Scientific satellite.

Contracting agency: Soviet Academy of Sciences.

Status: Operational.

Mission: Study low-energy radiation.

Performance: Launched into medium and high earth orbits.

Specifications: Dimensions — not disclosed. Power supply — solar cells.

Equipment: Mass spectrometer, low-energy proton detector, charged-particle traps and solar X ray measuring device.

History: Pairs of the satellite were launched in January and July, 1964. The first ranged out to 3,600 miles and the second as far as 41,000 miles. They were providing details of the Van Allen radiation belts.

ASTRONOMICAL SATELLITE (EUROPE)

Type: Unmanned scientific satellite.

Contracting agency: European Space Research Organization (ESRO).

Status: R&D.

Mission: Ultraviolet stellar spectroscopy.

Specifications: Weight — about 1,700 lbs. Launch — on top of Europa I.

Principal contractor: Prime — ESRO.

History: Scheduled to be launched about 1970. ESRO has scheduled a series of scientific satellites for launching in the late 1960's.

SPACE BOOSTERS

Launch of an Atlas-Agena D.
—NASA photograph

AGENA D (U.S.)

Type: Second-stage booster.

Contracting agency or military service: National Aeronautics and Space Administration, Air Force.

Status: Operational.

Mission: Used with modified Thor or Atlas first stage for orbital injection and with Atlas for lunar and planetary trajectories.

Performance: Thor-Agena D — boosts 1,600 lbs. into 100-mile orbit. Atlas-Agena D — boosts 5,000 lbs. into 100-mile orbit or 750 lbs. to escape velocity. Agena D is restartable, allowing vehicle to coast to desired height before injection into orbit.

Specifications: Stages — 2. Length — Thor-Agena D, 80.9 ft.; Thor-Agena B — 86 ft. Weight — about 123,000 lbs. Diameter — 5 ft. Length — Agena D only, 25 ft. Diameter — 5 ft. Weight (loaded) — 15,550 lbs. Propulsion — all liquid. Fuel — unsymmetrical dimethylhydrozine (UDMH) and inhibited red fuming nitric acid (IRFNA). Guidance — inertial.

Principal contractors: Prime — Lockheed. Propulsion — Bell Aerospace. Guidance — Minneapolis-Honeywell.

History: Thor-Agena A was used principally in the Air Force's Discoverer program, starting in late 1959. Switch was made to Agena B in 1961. NASA began using the Agena B in mid-1961 for a variety of satellite missions. Agena D is the improved successor to both earlier models.

CENTAUR (U.S.)

Type: Second-stage booster.

Contracting agency or military service: National Aeronautics and Space Administration, Air Force.

Status: Development.

Performance: Boost 8,500-lb. payload into 100-mile orbit, 2,300-lb. payload to escape velocity, 1,450-lb. payload onto trajectory to Mars or Venus.

Missions: Used with Atlas to launch Surveyor (lunar) and Mariner (planetary) probes.

Specifications: Stages — 2. Length — 30 ft. Diameter — 10 ft. Gross weight (Atlas-Centaur) — 291,000 lbs. Total thrust — 378,000 lbs. First stage — modified Atlas ICBM; fuel RP-1 and LOX. Second stage — twin engines; liquid hydrogen and LOX fuel. Guidance — inertial.

Principal contractors: Prime — Convair. Frame — Convair (both stages). Propulsion — Rocketdyne, first stage; Pratt & Whitney, second stage.

History: R&D on the second stage began in late 1959. There were major slippages in the program. The first successful test flight occurred in late 1963. Expected to be operational in 1966.

THOR-DELTA, THOR-ABLESTAR (U.S.)

Type: Two-stage boosters.

Contracting agency or military service: National Aeronautics and Space Administration, Air Force.

Status: Operational.

Mission: Satellite launching.

Performance: Delta — boosts 500 lbs. into 300-mile

Thor-Delta launch, 1964.

—NASA photograph

orbit. Ablestar — boosts 1,000 lbs. into 300-mile orbit.

Specifications: Over-all length — Delta, 92 ft.; Ablestar, 79 ft. Weight — Delta, 112,000 lbs.; Ablestar, 119,000 lbs. Diameter of Thor — 8 ft. Propulsion — Delta, 2 liquid stages, 1 solid; Ablestar, 2 liquid. Fuel — RP-1 and LOX for liquid stages. Guidance — inertial, radio command. Ablestar engine is restartable in space.

Principal contractors: Prime — Douglas for Delta and Thor stages; Aerojet for Ablestar vehicle. Guidance — BTL for Delta.

History: Various combinations of Thor boosters have been the mainstay of the early United States space program. Deltas are assigned to NASA's communications and weather satellite R&D programs, while the Ablestar has been used in the Navy's Transit navigational satellite and the Army's Courier communications satellite programs.

Delta (TAD) uses small solid rockets strapped to base for extra lifting power.

—Douglas Aircraft Co. photograph

TAT, TAD (U.S.)

Type: Advanced versions of Thor and Delta.

Contracting agency: National Aeronautics and Space Administration, Air Force.

Status: Operational.

Performance: Thrust Augmented Thor (TAT) payload — 1,800 lbs. into 300-mile orbit. Thrust Augmented Delta (TAD) — 1,100 lbs. into 300-mile orbit.

Specifications: Thor and Delta (see above). Three strap-on solid boosters added to make TAT and TAD. Total thrust of solids — 162,000 lbs.

Principal contractor: Solids — Thiokol. (See above for Thor and Delta.)

History: First flights in 1964.

SCOUT (U.S.)

Type: Lightweight satellite booster.

Contracting agency or military service: National Aeronautics and Space Administration, Air Force.

Status: Operational.

Mission: Launch small satellites and space probes.

Performance: Can boost 240-lb. payload to 345-mile orbit or 80-lb. payload to escape velocity.

Specifications: Length — 72 ft. Diameter — 40 in. Weight — 36,100 lbs. Stages — 4. Propulsion — all solid. Guidance — semi-inertial.

Principal contractors: Prime — LTV. Propulsion — Aerojet, Thiokol, and Hercules.

History: An outgrowth of the Polaris and Minuteman propulsion programs, Scout has been billed as the "poor man's" space booster, since the basic vehicle costs about 1 million dollars, against 2 to 4 million dollars for heavier boosters. First flight tests were made in 1960. The Air Force version is called Blue Scout and is being used chiefly to gather data for the Air Force space flight program. NASA is offering Scout to other nations for space research.

Diamant 2 in checkout tower.

DIAMANT 2 (FRANCE)

Type: Lightweight satellite booster.

Contracting agency: Centre National d'Etudes Spatiales (CNES).

Status: Flight testing.

Mission: Launching communications and scientific payloads into equatorial and polar orbits.

Performance: Can boost 200-plus-lb. payload to 350-mile circular orbit.

Specifications: Length — about 60 ft. Diameter — about 5 ft. Weight — 60,000 lbs. Stages — 3. Propulsion — all solid. Thrust — 88,200 lbs. Guidance — inertial.

Principal contractor: Prime — SEREB.

History: Development began in 1961. Forerunner of the French IRBM ordered by De Gaulle to give the nation a nuclear missile punch. An earlier version had liquid-fueled first stage. Launchings conducted from equatorial zone space flight center in French Guiana. The center was established in 1964.

ELDO (EUROPE)

Type: Satellite launch vehicle.

Contracting agency: European Launch Development Organization (ELDO).

Status: R&D.

Mission: Serve as launch vehicle for joint European Space Research Organization (ESRO) satellites.

Performance: Launch 1,000-lb. payload into 300-mile orbit.

Specifications: Stages — 3. First stage (Blue Streak) — 61.6 ft./10 ft.; weight — 192,000 lbs.; thrust — 300,000 lbs. Second stage — 18.8 ft./6 ft.; weight — 25,400 lbs.; thrust — 61,700 lbs. Third stage — 10.1 ft./6.5 ft.; thrust — 5,100 lbs.

Principal contractors: First stage — Hawker (U.K.). Second stage — SEREB (France). Third stage — ERNO (West Germany).

History: Work began on the Blue Streak as a 2,000-mile missile in 1957 and was canceled in January 1960. R&D was continued on the booster, however, as a possible space booster. In mid-1961, Britain made a tentative agreement with France, West Germany and other European nations to join in a co-operative space program expected to cost about 200 million dollars over 5 years. An advanced ELDO B is scheduled for development. Payload would be 1,500 lbs.

ROVER (U.S.)

Type: Nuclear rocket engine development program.

Contracting agency: National Aeronautics and Space Administration, Atomic Energy Commission (AEC).

Status: R&D.

Mission: Booster for interplanetary manned space flight.

Performance: Would be used initially as an upper-stage engine to propel heavy payloads in space.

Specifications: Not determined.

Principal contractors: AEC, Aerojet.

History: R&D began in 1959 toward a dual objective — a nuclear rocket engine that would perform basically like a conventional rocket engine and a flyable nuclear reactor that would act as the power source for various types of electrical and plasma rocket engines. First launch of a nuclear rocket called Nerva using liquid hydrogen as the propellant was originally planned for about 1966 or 1967. No flight program is scheduled. Ground tests have been successful.

HISTORIC SPACE SHOTS

Name and country	Weight in lbs.	Launch date & vehicle	Trajectory	Result
Sputnik I (U.S.S.R.)	184	10/4/57; N.A. (not available)	Orbit 65° to equator, 142/558 miles	First earth satellite; circled earth for 95 days
Explorer I (U.S.)	30.8	1/31/58; Jupiter C	Orbit 32° to equator, 217/1,155 miles	Discovered radiation belts; est. life 7–10 yrs.
Vanguard I (U.S.)	3.25	3/17/58; Vanguard	Orbit 34° to equator, 406/2,444 miles	Discovered earth is "pear-shaped"
Lunik II (U.S.S.R.)	780 (incl. final stage)	9/12/59; N.A.	Lunar impact	Achieved impact; radiation and magnetism measurements
Lunik III (U.S.S.R.)	about 614	10/4/59; N.A.	Earth-moon orbit, 25,000/292,000 miles	Took first picture of far side of moon; very long lifetime
Tiros I (U.S.)	270	4/1/60; Thor-Able	Earth orbit, 467/429 miles	Picture-taking weather satellite; est. life 50–100 yrs.
Transit IB (U.S.)	265	4/13/60; Thor-Ablestar	Earth orbit, 417/229 miles	First R&D navigational satellite; est. life 6 yrs.
Discoverer XIV (U.S.)	1,700	8/18/60; Thor-Agena	Polar orbit, 116/502 miles	Achieved first recovery of object ejected from orbit, a 300-lb. capsule
Cosmic Ship II (U.S.S.R.)	10,120	8/19/60; N.A.	Orbit 64° to equator, 190/211 miles	Achieved first recovery of dogs (2) and other specimens from orbit in capsule
Courier 1-B (U.S.)	500	10/4/60; Thor-Ablestar	Orbit 28° to equator, 604/750 miles	First delayed repeater communications satellite; est. life several years
Venus Probe (U.S.S.R.)	1,419	2/12/61; N.A.	Toward Venus	First launch of space probe from orbit (Sputnik VIII); radio failed en route
Vostok I (U.S.S.R.)	10,418	4/12/61; N.A.	Orbit 65° to equator, 108/187 miles	First manned orbital flight; one orbit
Mercury (U.S.)	2,987	2/20/62; Atlas D	Orbit 32.5° to equator, 100/163 miles	First U.S. manned orbital spacecraft; 3 orbits
Mariner II (U.S.)	570	8/27/62; Atlas-Agena B	Interplanetary	First successful probe of Venus
Ranger VII (U.S.)	800	7/28/64; Atlas-Agena B	Lunar	First closeup pictures of moon
Voskhod I (U.S.S.R.)	11,070	10/12/64; N.A.	Orbit 65° to equator, 100/255 miles	First 3-man crew; 16 orbits
Mariner IV (U.S.)	575	11/28/64; Atlas-Agena D	Earth to Mars	First closeup pictures of Mars, July 14, 1965
Voskhod II (U.S.S.R.)	11,000	3/18/65; N.A.	Orbit 65° to equator, 108/307 miles	First man to leave capsule in space
Gemini V (U.S.)	7,000	8/21/65; Titan II	Orbit 32.5° to equator, 100/219 miles	First manned flight in space for 8 days — time to moon and return

U.S. Air Force's principal space booster for manned and satellite missions—the Titan III-C. Rocket can lift 25,000 lbs.

—U.S. Air Force photograph

3

SPACE WEAPONS: FRONT LINE IN ORBIT

One of the larger politico-technical controversies of the decade of the 1960's is labeled "military uses of space."

The military — primarily the U.S. Air Force — have argued since the days of Sputnik I that they should have a major role in space. They contend that the future security of the country demands it.

Many influential scientists and administrators — primarily in NASA and the Defense Department — have argued that proven military requirements in space are limited. Moreover, they contend that most technology that might be needed for more extensive military space activities in the future can be developed in civilian programs.

To this relatively clear disagreement must be added the following muddying factors:

— Both the Air Force and NASA have a competitive organizational interest in obtaining responsibility for as large a piece of the national space program as possible.

— The prime motivating force behind the space program is fear of the Soviet Union and its space program. However, Congress and the public appear convinced that the Soviet space challenge is being met regardless of which government agency runs the program.

— The international environment of the 1960's makes it politically desirable for both the United States and Russia to conduct their space programs under the banner of scientific exploration.

— The assignment of most United States space activities to NASA makes new sizeable additions to an already large defense budget unnecessary.

The real question is whether the technology and experience that might be needed for future military space operations will indeed be obtained during the next five to ten years. Also underlying this question is the Air Force contention that it must go into space in order to determine what requirements for weapons it may have there.

A number of Air Force planners have argued that space is the potential high ground of tomorrow.

Control of near space — an area extending out from earth about 1,000 miles — would give man access to targets all over the world. It also might make possible a defense against nuclear-tipped missiles and thereby unbalance the United States-Soviet nuclear stalemate.

Much further in the future are the weapons that might be employed in cislunar space — the area encompassing the entire 240,000 miles to the moon — and in translunar or interplanetary space — the immense reaches beyond the moon in our solar system.

These weapons, if they come to pass, would be designed to attack other spacecraft and to defend themselves thousands of miles away in the cold blankness of space. Presumably, they might be used to struggle for control of space.

This is the nightmare that has plagued some

military planners when they watched Soviet progress in space. On the other hand, a number of influential scientists and military advisers have contended that such ideas appear to be technically and economically impractical.

Observers of the national argument over the value of military space programs can only conclude that except for the Air Force's Manned Orbiting Laboratory (MOL) program the fight has been going against the military. The lengthy necrology of military space programs speaks for itself.

Dozens of programs have died, shrunk into feeble continuing studies or disappeared into files where they have lived on only as names. Newer programs have been born only to exist in a state of permanent infancy.

Among the more prominent fatalities have been Dyna-Soar, a manned orbital space glider; Advent, a military communications satellite; Aerospace Plane, an air-space bomber; Nova, a 12-million-pound-thrust space booster. Finally, Saint, a satellite inspection and interception system, was reduced to a low-funded study program.

At the same time, the Air Force achieved an outstanding success with its Samos photo reconnaissance satellite.

Samos began as Discoverer, a historic program designed to test various components for military space systems. Discoverer XII ejected a capsule from orbit for the first time in 1960. The capsule was retrieved from the Pacific; later, Air Force planes retrieved capsules as they fell through the atmosphere.

The details of the Samos program have been highly classified. However, it has been reported that excellent photographs of the Soviet bloc have been taken on a continuing basis since the early 1960's.

The pictures changed American intelligence estimates of the number of ICBM's deployed by the U.S.S.R., showing the celebrated "missile gap" of 1960 to be in favor of the United States. Samos also detected Red China's gaseous diffusion plant, which produces U-235 for its atomic bombs.

There is an electronic eavesdropping version of Samos, the Ferret, which monitors Red military radio channels and could give warning of an impending attack.

The Russians apparently have developed a photo-reconnaissance satellite as part of their Cosmos program. Although they do not need it as much as the United States, there has been an important benefit. It provides knowledge of the effectiveness of Samos, permitting the Russians to cover up what they don't want observed.

One other military satellite that has succeeded is the Navy's Transit. Several are kept in orbit, beaming out radio signals that enable Polaris submarines to acquire an accurate navigational fix as to their exact position without having to surface. Knowing precisely where they are at all times is essential to the submarines' ability to fire their missiles on target.

Unlike the United States, the Russians have always openly declared their belief in the military potential of manned spacecraft.

The clear stamp of the Soviet Air Force has been on all flights of manned Soviet spacecraft. And Soviet leaders have repeatedly boasted that their manned spacecraft could just as well carry 50-megaton nuclear weapons.

Moreover, the pattern of manned launchings has followed, step by step, approximately the pattern that United States military men would follow if they were conducting a program aimed at developing the capability to operate manned military spacecraft in near space.

Early long flights of Vostoks piloted by Air Force cosmonauts were followed by flights that opened the way for the Russians to begin rendezvousing in orbit. The successful Soviet orbiting and landing of the three-man Voskhod I in October of 1964 opened the way for the orbiting for relatively long periods of small Soviet space stations.

The U.S. Air Force has stated that the operation of a manned space station for extended periods is the key to determining the future military role in space. And the Air Force has all but staked its own future in space on such a program.

The program — MOL — calls for sustaining men in space for about a month. A space station of this type would answer such questions as:

— How long can a man safely remain in orbit?

— Can a man perform work in orbit with his full faculties?

— If he can, how long can he do it?

— Will physiological changes such as loss of calcium from the bones occur after extended periods of weightlessness?

— How effectively can such military activities as reconnaissance and satellite interception be accomplished?

Concepts of large space stations.
—Douglas Aircraft Co. drawing

As Air Force Lt. Gen. James Ferguson, head of Air Force R&D, put it bluntly when speaking in support of MOL: "In a direct military sense, MOL will let us come to grips for the first time with the crucial question of the military usefulness of man in space."

Dr. Albert C. Hall, the Defense Department's Deputy Director for R&D, stated the case for an experimental manned space station with equal firmness: "We believe that we should purchase insurance against the possibility that a manned operational system may be required in the middle 1970's. This insurance will take the form of a flight test system to determine man's effectiveness in performing useful military functions in space."

The Air Force awarded development contracts on MOL in the summer of 1965. The schedule called for orbiting the first MOL space stations in 1968.

Nose fairing being installed on Voskhod I. The cone, with instrument hatch open, protects the spacecraft during launch through atmosphere and is jettisoned in orbit.

—Novosti from Sovfoto

MILITARY MANNED SPACECRAFT

VOSKHOD (U.S.S.R.)

Type: Orbital manned spacecraft.

Military service: Air Force.

Status: Operational.

Mission: Investigate strategic uses of space; act as prototype for building space stations and lunar spacecraft.

Capacity: A crew of three or more.

Performance: Designed for flights lasting about two weeks. Equipped with air lock to permit cosmonauts to leave craft in space; parachute landing system. Some maneuverability in space. Employs 1.4-million-lb.-thrust booster.

Specifications: Length over-all — about 25 ft. Diameter — about 13 ft. Weight — 11,500 lbs. Apparently divided into a command module with heat shield for re-entry and a service module where oxygen, batteries and other stores are kept. Has oxygen-nitrogen air system maintained at 1 to 1.2 atmospheres.

Instrumentation: Radios and TV for monitoring of experiments. Navigation panel includes small globe which revolves to show true position of craft in orbit. Craft can be oriented optically to correct retro-fire position.

History: First tested October 13, 1964, with three-man crew, which included one cosmonaut, a doctor and an engineer. The 16-orbit flight lasted a little over 24 hours. On March 26, 1965, a two-man crew demonstrated how one of them could exit into space on a rope. Air lock was used to decompress cosmonaut before he switched to 100% oxygen at .5 atmosphere in his spacesuit. Voskhod flights began after six flights of the smaller, one-man, Vostok, which had a flight duration maximum of five days. Launchings were from Tyura Tam cosmodrome and landings were made in the Soviet mid-continent.

Voskhod II with saucer-shaped airlock used by Alexei Leonov for his space walk. The airlock is retractable and contains a hatch for egress from the cabin.

—Sovfoto

GEMINI B (U.S.)

Type: Orbital spacecraft.

Military service: Air Force.

Status: R&D.

Mission: Investigate strategic uses of space; serve as ferry from Manned Orbiting Laboratory (MOL).

Capacity: Two-man crew.

Performance: Designed for flights lasting about two weeks. Hatches permit astronauts to exit into space. Highly maneuverable in space. Will carry military reconnaissance and other experiments. Launch vehicle is the Titan 3-A or Titan 3-C.

Specifications: Same as Gemini A, except for hatch in heat shield.

Principal contractors: Same as Gemini A.

History: Study project on the feasibility of a Gemini B-MOL was started in 1963 following the dropping of the Air Force's Dyna-Soar, a one-man space glider.

Manned Orbiting Laboratory (MOL) and modified Gemini B capsule in artist's concept.

—U.S. Air Force photograph

MOL— MANNED ORBITING LABORATORY (U.S.)

Type: Orbital space station.

Military service: Air Force.

Status: R&D.

Mission: Investigate strategic uses of space and determine man's ability to function in space for up to 30 days.

Capacity: Two-man crew.

Performance: Designed to maintain two men in "shirtsleeve" environment for 30 days. Will fly in 100- to 200-mile earth orbit. Launched aboard Titan 3-C in combination with Gemini B. Astronauts ride into space in the Gemini and transfer into MOL through hatch in heat shield. MOL is left in orbit when astronauts return to earth aboard Gemini.

Specifications: Length — about 41 ft. Diameter — 10 ft. Weight — about 19,000 lbs. Internal volume — about 2,500 cu. ft. Cabin environment — undecided.

Principal contractors: MOL air frame — Douglas. Experiments — GE. Re-entry capsules (Gemini B) — McDonnell.

History: Canister-shaped MOL concept was proposed following cancellation in late 1963 of the Air Force's Dyna-Soar space glider. Feasibility contracts were let in 1964. Prime contractors selected in 1965. First launchings unmanned MOL's scheduled in 1968; manned in 1969. Eight flights (5 manned) scheduled. Total cost estimated to be $1.5 billion.

MILITARY SATELLITES

Discoverer readied for launching at Vandenberg Air Force Base, Calif.

—Lockheed Aircraft Corp. photograph

DISCOVERER (U.S.)

Type: Experimental satellite for development of military space weapons.

Military service: Air Force.

Status: Operational.

Performance: Orbits 1,600-lb. payloads in 300-mile polar trajectories, ejects from orbit capsules capable of re-entry and recovery.

Specifications: Modified Agena B length — 19.2 ft.; weight — 1,600 lbs.; diameter — 5 ft. Re-entry capsule length — 27 in.; diameter — 33 in.; weight — about 300 lbs. Booster — Thor.

Instrumentation: IR, high-resolution photographic cameras, TV, and other devices being designed for Midas and Samos.

Principal contractors: Prime — Lockheed. Capsule — GE.

History: First conceived in 1956. R&D began on Discoverer in 1957. Almost 30 Discoverer satellites were launched between 1959 and the end of 1961. Six of the capsules were recovered — the first from Discoverer XII on August 11, 1960, after 17 passes around the earth. Although this capsule had to be retrieved from the sea, the Air Force subsequently perfected a system of "snatching" the capsules while they were still floating down under a parachute.

SATELLITE INTERCEPTOR (U.S.)

Type: Surface-to-orbit.

Military service: Air Force.

Status: R&D.

Mission: Destroy orbital bombs.

Deployment: Location — Johnston Island, 1,000 miles southwest of Hawaii.

Performance: Range — about 1,000 miles. Speed — 18,000 m.p.h.

Specifications: Not disclosed. Warhead — nuclear. Launched by Thrust Augmented Thor.

Principal contractors: Prime, launch vehicle — Douglas. Others not disclosed.

History: Development began in 1961. President Johnson declared the weapon operational at the start of his campaign in 1964. However, subsequent Congressional testimony disclosed the weapon was never established on a combat footing. It was retained as an R&D instrument and obtained in-space photos of some Soviet Cosmos and Voskhod spacecraft.

START (U.S.)

Type: Orbit-to-earth.

Military service: Air Force.

Status: R&D.

Mission: Return reconnaissance payloads from orbit, investigate maneuverable re-entry for spacecraft and ICBM warheads. Name stands for Spacecraft Technology and Advanced Re-entry Test.

Performance: Not disclosed. Launched by Atlas-Agena.

Specifications: Configuration — wingless, V-shaped lift-

Start configuration.

—Martin Co. drawing

ing body. Equipped with gas jets and flaps for re-entry. Designed with ablative coating to survive 3,000-degree heat.

Principal contractor: Prime, spacecraft — Martin.

History: Program initiated in 1965 as follow-up to Project Asset, which investigated re-entry configurations.

SAMOS (U.S.)

Type: Reconnaissance satellite.

Military service: Air Force.

Status: Operational.

Mission: Maintain photographic surveillance of Russia. Electronic eavesdropping version called Ferret also operational.

Performance: Polar orbit of several hundred miles. Launched by Atlas-Agena B. Orbital life of several years. Employs capsule ejection system for return of data to earth. There is probably more than one capsule.

Specifications: Length — about 20 ft. Diameter — 5 ft. Weight — about 5,000 lbs. Capsule weight — about 300 lbs.

Instrumentation: High-resolution cameras and television relay.

Principal contractor: Prime — Lockheed.

History: R&D was started in 1958 and then accelerated in a top-priority crash program following the down-

Samos.

—U.S. Air Force photograph

ing of the U-2 aerial reconnaissance plane over Russia in May 1960 — an incident that caused the suspension of U-2 flights. Samos — often called "spy in the sky" — is reported to identify small objects on the ground, including people. First successful launching of an R&D model took place January 31, 1961. Provided intelligence on Soviet ICBM deployment that reversed early "missile gap" estimates.

ICBM ALARM (U.S.)

Type: Early-warning satellite.

Military service: Air Force.

Status: R&D.

Mission: Detect ICBM launchings at moment of blastoff.

Performance: Polar orbit, about 300 nautical miles. Launched by Atlas-Agena B. Orbital life — 1 to 2 years.

Specifications: Length — 22 ft. Diameter — 5 ft. Weight — about 5,000 lbs.

Instrumentation: IR scanner in nose; data link telemetry and tape-fed programer. Information is relayed to ground stations.

Principal contractor: Prime — Lockheed.

History: First conceived in 1956; R&D began in 1957. First flight tests began in 1960. Formerly called Midas.

COSMOS (U.S.S.R.)

Type: All-purpose spacecraft.

Military service: Air Force.

Status: Operational.

Mission: Primarily intended to check on what United States Samos satellites are photographing. However, Cosmos label also has been applied to trial Vostok and Voskhod craft and to numerous lunar and planetary probes that failed.

Performance: Range — earth orbital. Able to eject payloads from orbit.

Specifications: Not disclosed but apparently vary from payload to payload.

History: Cosmos 1, orbited May 25, 1962, was the first Soviet spacecraft launched from its Kapustin Iar cosmodrome. Craft went into an orbit inclined 49 degrees to the equator in comparison to 65-degree inclination from Tyura Tam. More than 60 craft bearing Cosmos name were launched through 1965.

POLYOT (U.S.S.R.)

Type: Maneuverable satellite.

Military service: Air Force.

Status: Operational.

Mission: Apparently to investigate orbital change thrust requirements preparatory to building a manned space station.

Performance: Not disclosed.

Specifications: Not disclosed.

History: Polyot 1, launched November 1, 1963, performed dogleg maneuver that put it into an orbit inclined 59 degrees to the equator. Polyot 2, launched April 12, 1964, performed virtually the same maneuver. Neither was regarded as particularly startling.

TRANSIT (U.S.)

Type: Navigational satellite.

Military service: Navy.

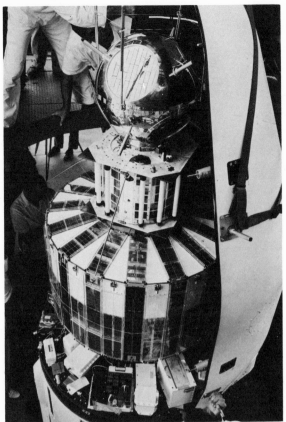

Transit (bottom) with piggyback riders.
—U.S. Navy photograph

Status: Operational.

Mission: Provide a continuous navigational reference point, particularly for submerged Polaris submarines.

Deployment: The system involves deployment of 4 satellites at all times — 2 in polar orbit and 2 in equatorial orbit.

Performance: Orbital height — about 500 nautical miles. Launched by Thor-Ablestar.

Specifications: Configuration — hatbox-shaped. Operational weight — about 50 lbs. Power supply — solar cells, storage batteries, and nuclear generator.

Instrumentation: Radio beacon transmitter.

Principal contractor: Prime — APL.

History: R&D was started in 1958. The Transit system involves the use of complex ground computation and shipboard equipment to translate the satellite signals into a useful piece of information — since both the ship and the satellite are moving, and not necessarily in the same direction. While surface ships may find Transit useful, only Polaris subs really need it. They must operate below the surface in radio silence — receiving but not transmitting. The Transit beacon provides reliable crosscheck on the other navigational aids aboard the subs.

Syncom-type military Comsat.
—U.S. Army photograph

MILITARY COMSAT (U.S.)

Type: Active repeater.

Military service: Air Force, Defense Communications Agency.

Status: R&D.

Configuration: 18 to 24 satellites in random orbits, 6,000 to 8,000 miles apogee, to provide continuous voice and telecommunications around the globe.

Specifications: Not disclosed.

Principal contractor: Prime — Philco.

History: Program was initiated late in 1964 after many false starts, including Army's Advent comsat which was canceled when it grew too heavy for available

39

boosters. NASA transferred its two Syncom comsats to the military in 1965, providing some interim service. However, the full comsat system was not expected to be orbited until 1967. It was scheduled aboard some of the final Titan III-C test flights and the satellites were to be strung out six at a time in space.

NUCLEAR DETECTION SATELLITE (U.S.)

Type: Passive detector.

Military service: Air Force, AEC.

Status: Operational.

Mission: Report any nuclear tests in space.

Performance: Launched in pairs into orbits ranging more than 60,000 miles from earth. Launched by Atlas Agena.

Specifications: Weight — 480 lbs. Configuration — 20-sided icosahedron. Carries 20 X-ray, gamma and neutron detectors capable of spotting blasts millions of miles in deep space.

Principal contractor: Prime — TRW, STL.

History: First pair launched in 1963, second in 1964, third in 1965. Formerly called Vela Hotel.

MILITARY BOOSTERS

TITAN III-A, C, X (U.S.)

Type: Heavy launch vehicle.

Military service: Air Force.

Status: Flight testing.

Mission: Launch MOL, Gemini B and military satellites into earth orbit.

Performance: III-A can launch 8,000-lb. payload plus maneuverable transtage engine into earth orbit; III-C can launch 25,000 lbs. into earth orbit or put 5,000 lbs. on moon; III-X in combination with Centaur stage can orbit 10–15,000 lbs. Thrust — 546,000 to 3,046,000 lbs.

Specifications: Titan II, a two-stage liquid-propelled rocket, forms the "core" for all three vehicles. In Titan III-A, a 16,000-lb.-thrust transtage is added to the top of Titan II; in Titan III-C, two 1.25-million-lb.-thrust solid rockets are strapped on either side of the "core" and a transtage is added; in III-X, Centaur is substituted for transtage — solid assist rockets also may be strapped on. Launch weights — 370,000 lbs. (III-A); 1,400,000 lbs. (III-C); about 500,000 lbs. (III-X).

Principal contractors: Prime, launch vehicle — Martin. Liquid engines — Aerojet. Solid engines — United Aircraft. Guidance — GE with Burroughs.

History: Development of 10-ft.-diameter segmented solid rockets started in 1962 for III-C. Test program involving 12 vehicles began in 1965. Total development cost of the Titan III's three versions was estimated at more than 800 million dollars.

Titan III-A launch, 1964.
—U.S. Air Force photograph

HEAVY LAUNCH VEHICLE (U.S.S.R.)

Type: Multistage booster.

Developing agency: Air Force.

Status: Operational.

Mission: Orbit space stations and make deep-space probes.

Performance: Boosts 27,000 lbs. or more into low earth orbit.

Specifications: Thrust — about 2.5 million lbs. Dimensions — not disclosed.

History: Orbited 27,000-lb. Proton I scientific space station in July 1965. Expected to be employed to orbit manned space stations and perform rendezvous maneuver for refueling lunar-bound spacecraft.

Big Brother.
—Aviation Week and Space
Technology photograph

BIG BROTHER (U.S.S.R.)*

Type: Heavy launch vehicle.

Military service: Air Force.

Status: Operational.

Mission: Launch Voskhod and Vostok spacecraft.

Performance: Payload — more than 20,000 lbs. into earth orbit. Total thrust (max.) — about 1.4 million lbs.

Specifications: Length — about 105 ft. Width — 13.5 ft. Stages — 3. Propulsion — liquid. Thrust — 850,000 to 1.2 million lbs.

History: For Vostok flights the booster was rated at about 850,000 lbs. thrust, indicating it was considerably altered and uprated for Voskhod. Soviets were believed building a 3- to 5-million-lb.-thrust version for orbiting large space stations and lunar exploration. Soviets in 1965 said Big Brother could orbit H-bombs. (See Scrag ICBM.)

*NATO designation.

Titan III-C launch concept.
—United Aircraft drawing

Polaris A-3 firing by **U.S.S. Tecumseh.**
—U.S. Navy photograph

4

STRATEGIC MISSILES:
THE GREAT DETERRENT

The ICBM became the ace of spades in the military deck of cards in the mid-1960's.

Both the United States and the Soviet Union continue to maintain large fleets of manned bombers. And they are expected to do so well into the 1970's and probably longer. But the weapon that has turned the Cold War into the Frozen War is the nuclear-tipped intercontinental ballistic missile.

America and Russia face each other across the globe. Each is armed with enough great missiles to obliterate the other. Each knows it. The result is a long-predicted balance of terror: a strategic stalemate.

No military adventure, no matter how small, can be conducted today without taking into account the awesome power of these great weapons. Their terrifying shadows fall across every continent.

By the push of a button, a nuclear bomb of from one to more than ten megatons in explosive power — the equivalent of more than one to ten million tons of TNT — can be hurled 6,000 miles in about 30 minutes. The potency of such a weapon is staggering. A ten-megaton warhead can gouge a crater 250 feet deep and about one-half mile in diameter. The fireball would have a diameter of more than two and a half miles. Both American and Soviet ICBM's are estimated to be accurate enough to strike well within two miles of their targets.

For obvious reasons the precise number of United States and Soviet ICBM's ready for launch at any particular moment is one of the most carefully maintained secrets in the world. However, at the end of 1965 the United States claimed an overwhelming lead.

An estimated force of 800 Minuteman ICBM's were on operational status in buried silos widely scattered across the western United States. In addition, 54 huge Titan II's stood in their buried silos in Arizona, Kansas and Arkansas. And somewhere beneath the world's oceans within easy striking distance of the Soviet heartland cruised up to 41 nuclear-powered submarines carrying a total of 656 Polaris missiles.

Russia opposed this mighty force with an estimated total of 200 ICBM's deployed in Russia. Soviet submarines armed with an estimated 100 relatively short-range missiles cruised within striking distance of United States shores. And hundreds of 600- to 2,200-mile-range Shyster and Sandal missiles were deployed within striking distance of Western Europe, the Middle East, Red China, and Japan. These were the same missiles that turned up in Cuba in 1962.

By the mid-1960's, the United States became so confident of its lead that it had deactivated its first-generation IRBM's — the Thors and Jupiters based in the United Kingdom, Italy and Turkey — and its first generation of ICBM's — 132 Atlases and 45 Titan I's.

At the same time, the United States continued to build Minutemen and Polarises.

The total planned force of Minutemen was set at 1,000. The total force of Polaris submarines — each armed with 16 missiles — was set at 41. Moreover, plans called for developing greatly improved versions of both missiles — the Poseidon and the advanced Minuteman II — by the early 1970's. The Johnson Administration began the second half of the 1960's with expressions of confidence that such a force was more than enough to deter the Communist bloc from making a nuclear attack on the United States.

As the Secretary of Defense told Congress: "Based on the projected threat for the early 1970's . . . our calculations show that even after absorbing a first strike, our already authorized strategic missile force, if it were directed against the aggressor's urban areas, could cause more than 100 million fatalities and destroy about 80 per cent of his industrial capacity."

This vast destruction would be caused by missiles alone. And it was contended that the prospect of such destruction was "unacceptable" to the Kremlin. In other words, the price of a sneak nuclear attack on the United States would be too high. Russia, therefore, would be deterred.

There is no question that the cost has been tremendous. The Atlas alone cost about 2 billion dollars to develop. Each squadron of nine Atlas missiles cost between 130 million dollars and 150 million dollars to produce and turn over to the Strategic Air Command. The estimated cost of developing Polaris and advanced Polaris models is expected to top 2 billion dollars. The cost of each late-model Polaris-launching submarine is nearly 115 million dollars. The cost of Titan I and Titan II was somewhat higher than the Atlas. The cost of the Minuteman was about 5 billion dollars.

As the design of United States ICBM's has advanced, the method of deployment has advanced, as well, from highly vulnerable "soft" sites to highly invulnerable "hard" ones. The first operational Atlases at Vandenberg stood exposed in gantries much like the test gantries at Cape Kennedy. These missiles were extremely vulnerable to an attack, and the design for the launcher was quickly discarded. The configuration of the Atlas sites then went through a three-step evolution.

The first step had the nine Atlases in each squadron stretched out in coffin-shaped buildings in dispersed groups of three, with many additional buildings. This design still left the missiles vulnerable to even a not-so-near miss by a nuclear weapon. The second step — called "Hollywood hard" — compressed most of the equipment into one building and buried it at surface level. Also, the missiles were deployed separately instead of in groups of three. This left them vulnerable only to a relatively near miss. Finally, deep holes looking like inverted silos were dug into the ground so the missiles could be deployed individually at widely dispersed points. This was expected to make them invulnerable to almost anything but a direct hit.

From the beginning, the Titans were intended to be deployed in underground silos, and huge, sprawling bases were buried with them. The ten-story silos, containing elevators to raise the missiles for firing, are connected by great 12-foot-wide steel tunnels to dome-shaped hangars and control centers — a small city deep in the earth. The Titan II base is somewhat simpler, because the Titan II can be fired directly from its silo without elevating it to the surface.

Much of the complexity of Atlas and Titan bases was made necessary by their intricate systems for pumping liquid fuel into the missiles. The Minuteman base is far simpler because, among other reasons, the fuel — a solid — is already in the missile. Each squadron has 50 missiles, which can be fired directly from silos deployed at widely dispersed points. For each ten, one command post is buried underground at another dispersed point. The Minutemen themselves are monitored completely by machine. No missilemen are stationed at the silos. The missiles are launched by remote control from the command posts. If maintenance or repairs become necessary, lights flash on at the command post control boards, and special squads are dispatched to the appropriate silos by helicopter or car.

A plan for mobile Minutemen — actively pursued but now killed — called for deploying the missiles in special railroad cars. Missile trains with three to five missiles plus command cars, power cars, communication cars, and cars with living accommodations for the crews were to prowl the nation's rail network in an apparently random manner. Kept moving, the missiles would become even harder to locate and destroy in a surprise attack.

In essence, the Minuteman is a land-based and

consequently more exposed version of the solid-fueled Polaris. Each Polaris submarine hidden beneath the sea carries 16 missiles on approximately 60-day-long patrols. The submarines operate at secret stations somewhere within striking distance of the Soviet Union. After two months on patrol in their prescribed areas, the submarines rendezvous with their tenders, undergo any needed overhauling, take on supplies and a fresh crew, and return to their stations.

The obsolescent Hound Dogs are the most mobile of all strategic weapon systems in that they are carried by intercontinental-range aircraft. The Hound Dog is vulnerable to interception by advanced air defense weapons such as surface-to-air and air-to-air missiles. Also, its launching platform has relatively short endurance. Even with aerial refueling, the B-52 bomber can remain in the air at most only a few days. Therefore, some Air Force planners would like to develop a nuclear-powered bomber as a missile carrier. Such a bomber — nicknamed the Camel — would be able to remain on patrol for more than a week at a time and carry six to ten missiles.

Possibly the foreseeable ultimate in strategic missiles this side of space would be what some Air Force planners once called Midgetman. This would be an ICBM so greatly reduced in size that it could be deployed relatively cheaply by the thousands either in fixed silos or in trucks that might operate both overland and on the vast United States highway system. One of the prime requirements for such a weapon would be the development, through further nuclear testing in caves or space, of a more powerful yet still lighter nuclear warhead.

Some missile experts believe such a weapon could be developed within five years. If it is done, the long-range ballistic missile will have come full circle. It will return to the concept of the old German V-2's and the Meillerwagens that raced them along the back roads of France in the black nights of 1944.

LAND-BASED ICBM's

TITAN II (U.S.)

Type: Surface-to-surface.
Military service and designation: Air Force (LGM-25C).
Performance: Range — more than 9,000 nautical miles. Speed — more than 17,000 m.p.h. Apogee — more than 600 miles.

Titan II gets away from Cape Kennedy pad.
—U. S. Air Force photograph

Specifications: Length — 102 ft. Diameter — 10 ft. Launch weight — 300,000 lbs. Guidance — inertial. Warhead — nuclear. Propulsion — liquid; storable liquid (hydrazine and nitrogen tetroxide). Stages — 2. Total thrust — 530,000 lbs. (first stage, 430,000 lbs.; second stage, about 100,000 lbs.). Reaction time — 1 minute.

Principal contractors: Prime — Martin. Frame — Martin. Guidance — AC Spark Plug. Propulsion — Aerojet. Re-entry vehicle — GE.

History: R&D began in late 1955 on Titan I. The first successful flight took place February 6, 1959. The missile became initially operational at Lowry AFB near Denver, Colorado, in the fall of 1961. Forty-five of the missiles were deployed at a total of five bases. They were deactivated in 1965. Meantime, R&D on Titan II began in mid-1960. The cost of the Titan program is estimated to have been about the same total as the Atlas — nearly 4 billion dollars. One nine-missile Titan squadron, exclusive of R&D, is estimated to cost about 138 million dollars. Titan II also has a major role as a space booster both in its military configuration and as the main stage of Titan III.

Combat Titan II at McConnell Air Force Base, Kansas.
—U.S. Air Force photograph

DEPLOYMENT

Total squadrons authorized: 6.

Bases authorized: 3.

Squadron strength: 9 missiles (plus one spare).

Authorized total number of missiles on launchers: 54.

Total deployment completed: December 1963.

Titan II Bases

Davis-Monthan AFB, Tucson, Ariz. Two squadrons — 18 missiles, hard, dispersed, launched in silo.

McConnell AFB, Wichita, Kan. Two squadrons — 18 missiles, hard, dispersed, launched in silo.

Little Rock AFB, Little Rock, Ark. Two squadrons — 18 missiles, hard, dispersed, launched in silo.

Minuteman I roars over Pacific from Vandenberg Air Force Base silo.

—Boeing Co. photograph

MINUTEMAN (U.S.)

Type: Surface-to-surface (fixed base and mobile).

Military service and designation: Air Force (LGM-30A, B, F).

Status: Operational.

Performance: Range — 5,500 nautical miles. Speed — more than 15,000 m.p.h. Apogee — about 600 miles.

Specifications: Length — 54-60 ft. Diameter — about 6 ft. Launch weight — 69,000 lbs. Guidance — inertial. Warhead — nuclear. Propulsion — solid. Stages — 3. Total thrust — more than 120,000 lbs. Reaction time — less than 60 seconds.

Principal contractors: Major — Boeing. Frame — Boeing. Guidance — Autonetics. Propulsion — Boeing (first stage); Aerojet (second stage); Hercules (third stage). Re-entry vehicle — Avco and GE.

History: R&D began in 1958 on the Air Force's second-generation ICBM, the Minuteman. Plans called for developing a missile that could be deployed both in widely dispersed, underground "tubes" and aboard special trains that would operate on the nation's railroad network. However, R&D on the train-based Minuteman was indefinitely slowed down while top-priority work on the fixed-base Minuteman continued. The first Minuteman squadron became operational at Malmstrom AFB, Mont., in late 1962. The first Minuteman to be launched successfully soared down the Atlantic Missile Range February 1, 1961. The launching was particularly significant. For the first time in a big missile program, all stages in the initial firing were live ones and ignited. The expected cost of the Minuteman program has followed the usual trend of rising as the development program nears completion. The latest figures estimated that the total cost of deploying 12 "I" squadrons was about 1.8 billion dollars, or an astonishingly thrifty 3 million dollars per missile. Greatly improved Minuteman II with Mark 12 warhead has greater accuracy and payload. Estimated cost of producing, deploying and maintaining a Minuteman II over a five-year period: 6 million dollars.

DEPLOYMENT

Squadrons authorized: 20 (fixed site).

Bases authorized: 6 (fixed site).

Squadron strength: 50 missiles (fixed site).

Authorized total number of missiles on launchers: 1,000.

Operational missiles on launchers in 1966: More than 800.

Minuteman I Bases

Malmstrom AFB, Great Falls, Mont. Three squadrons — 150 missiles, hard, dispersed, launched in silo.

Ellsworth AFB, Rapid City, S.D. Three squadrons — 150 missiles, hard, dispersed, launched in silo.

Minot AFB, Minot, N.D. Three squadrons — 150 missiles, hard, dispersed, launched in silo.

Whiteman AFB, Knob Noster, Mo. Three squadrons — 150 missiles, hard, dispersed, launched in silo.

Warren AFB, Cheyenne, Wyo. Three squadrons — 150 missiles, hard, dispersed, launched in silo.

Minuteman II Bases

Grand Forks AFB, N.D. Three squadrons — 150 missiles, hard, dispersed, launched in silo.

Malmstrom AFB (see above).

SSBS-1 (FRANCE)

Type: Surface-to-surface.

Military service: Air Force.

Status: R&D.

Deployment: None.

Performance: Range — 2,300 nautical miles.

Specifications: Length — about 60 ft. Diameter — 3.5 ft. Weight — about 50,000 lbs. Stages — 2. Guidance — inertial. Propulsion — solid. Warhead — nuclear.

Principal contractor: SEREB.

History: Development began in 1960. An early version of the missile is the Diamant 2 space booster.

Russia's single-stage ICBM's on parade.
—Tass photograph

ICBM's (U.S.S.R.)

The Soviets have displayed three intercontinental ballistic missiles over the years in Moscow parades. A certain evolution is apparent. They have moved from a single-stage liquid-fueled missile to a two-stage liquid and then to a multistage solid rocket. The evolution is comparable to the U.S. progression from Atlas to Titan I and then to the modern Minuteman.

Scrags, 1965.
—Novosti Press Agency photograph

47

SCRAG*

Type: Surface-to-surface.

Military service: Air Force.

Status: Operational, but probably being phased out.

Deployment: See Soviet ICBM bases (below).

Performance: Range — 6,000-plus miles. Speed — 15,000 m.p.h.

Specifications: Length — 88 ft. Diameter — 9 ft. Launch weight — 240,000 lbs. Stages — 1. Guidance — radio command. Propulsion — LOX and kerosene. Thrust — about 550,000 lbs. Warhead — nuclear.

History: Development of this first Soviet ICBM apparently began in 1949 or 1950. It was designed to carry a 9,000- to 10,000-lb. warhead, the weight of early atom bombs. First 5,000-mile flight was achieved in 1957. It became the Soviet space flight booster. See Military Boosters.

*NATO designation.

Soviet two-stage liquid-fueled ICBM.
—Novosti Press Agency photograph

TWO-STAGE ICBM

Type: Surface-to-surface.

Military service: Air Force.

Status: Operational.

Deployment: See Soviet ICBM bases (below).

Performance: Range — 6,000-plus miles. Speed — 15,000 m.p.h.

Specifications: Length — about 80 ft. First-stage diameter — 10 ft. Second-stage diameter — 9 ft. Launch weight — about 250,000 lbs. Stages — 2. Guidance — probably radio inertial. Propulsion — LOX and kerosene. Thrust — about 600,000 lbs. Warhead — nuclear.

History: This missile was unveiled in 1964. It appears to represent considerable technical improvement, both in performance and in handling on the ground. It is carried on a trailer that also acts as an erector, indicating that it is designed for quick set-up and launch from a prepared above-ground pad.

Savage or Little Sister, 1965.
—Novosti Press Agency photograph

SAVAGE or LITTLE SISTER*

Type: Surface-to-surface.

Military service: Air Force.

Status: Operational.

Deployment: See Soviet ICBM bases (below).

Performance: Range — probably 8,000-plus miles. Speed — 17,000 m.p.h.

Specifications: Length — about 70 ft. Diameter — about 8 ft. Launch weight — undisclosed. Stages — 3. Guidance — probably inertial. Propulsion — solid. Thrust — not disclosed. Warhead — nuclear.

History: Development of this missile, a counterpart of the U.S. Minuteman, has been reported under way since 1961. The Soviets have paraded a large container showing four nozzles of a solid-fueled booster at one end; it may have been a model of this rocket.

*NATO designation.

SOVIET ICBM BASES

Neither the Russians nor United States intelligence have disclosed the precise location of Soviet big-missile bases. They apparently found their early single-stage ICBM difficult to maintain, however, and deployed only about 35 in above-ground launchers. They had the industrial capacity to turn out several hundred and it was on this production estimate that the celebrated "missile gap" of the early 1960's was founded. Development of a multistage solid ICBM indicates they are in the process of building silo-type underground launchers. It seems likely that, as great believers in mobility, they have built a number of camouflaged concrete surface pads for the easily transported and erected two-stage ICBM. These pads are probably near military installations where the missiles are stored. It is widely believed that the Russians have missiles near their Tyura Tam and Kapustin Iar cosmodromes, and in bases north of Moscow, in the Urals and on the Kamchatka Peninsula on the Pacific Ocean.

IRBM's (U.S.)

The United States has discontinued land-based intermediate-range ballistic missiles as a strategic weapon. Four wings of 1,500-mile Thors (60 missiles) were furnished Britain's Royal Air Force starting in 1959. The missiles were deactivated in 1964. Two squadrons of 1,500-mile Jupiters (30 missiles) were furnished Italy in 1961; one squadron (15 missiles) was deployed in Turkey in 1962. All Jupiters were retired and scrapped in 1964. More than 5 billion dollars was spent starting in 1955 to develop the nearly identical missiles as the Air Force, with the Thor, sought to wrest control of the strategic missile mission away from the Army. The Air Force won. Deployment of the missiles was strictly a stop-gap measure until the Air Force and Navy built up their ICBM and Polaris forces. Both Thors and Jupiters were installed in highly vulnerable surface pads and had slow reaction times (15 minutes or more).

In 1962, the Air Force began developing an MMRBM (Mobile Mid-Range Ballistic Missile) designed for launch from trucks and barges. The 300- to 1,500-mile missile was a competitor of the Polaris. The program was terminated in 1965.

IRBM's (U.S.S.R.)

SANDAL-2*

Type: Surface-to-surface.

Military service: Air Force.

Status: Operational.

Deployment: With mobile missile forces.

Performance: Range — about 2,200 miles. Speed — about 9,000 m.p.h.

Specifications: Length — about 65 ft. Diameter — 5 ft. Launch weight — about 160,000 lbs. Stages — 1. Guidance — radio command. Propulsion — liquid. Thrust — about 220,000 lbs. Warhead — nuclear.

History: Three battalions of Sandals were deployed in Cuba during 1962, precipitating a crisis with the

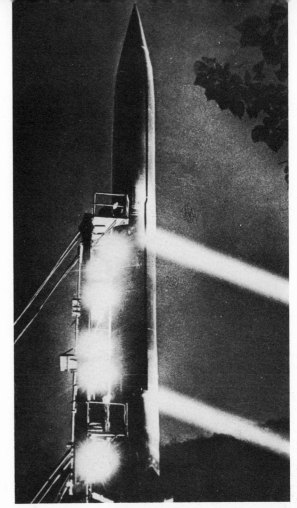

Soviet Sandal-2 IRBM on launch pad somewhere in Russia. Photo has been retouched by Russians.
—Tass photograph

United States. The Soviets are believed to have more than 300 of these missiles. They must be launched from a previously prepared site so they can be aligned properly in relation to their targets.

* NATO designation.

SNARK*

Type: Submarine-to-surface.

Military service: Navy.

Status: Operational.

Deployment: Aboard both nuclear and conventionally powered subs.

Performance: Range — about 1,200 miles. Speed — about 6,000 m.p.h.

Specifications: Length — about 34 ft. Diameter — 5 ft. Launch weight — 62,000 lbs. Stages — 2. Guidance — inertial. Propulsion — solid. Thrust — about 86,000 lbs. Warhead — nuclear.

History: This new missile, unveiled in 1964, apparently is rapidly replacing an early Snark, which was 46 ft. in length and probably liquid-fueled. It is very much like Polaris and may be launched from a submerged submarine.

* NATO designation.

49

Nuclear-powered submarine **Robert E. Lee,** fourth of Polaris fleet.

SEABORNE

POLARIS (U.S.)

Type: Submarine- or surface-ship-launched IRBM, surface-to-surface.

Military service and designation: Navy (UGM-27A, B, C).

Status: Operational (A-1 model, A-2 model, A-3 model). R&D (Poseidon).

Performance: Range — 1,200 nautical miles (A-1); 1,500 nautical miles (A-2); 2,500 nautical miles (A-3). Speed — about 8,000 m.p.h. Apogee — about 400 miles (A-1); about 500 miles (A-3).

Specifications: Length — 28 ft. (A-1); 30.5 ft. (A-2 and A-3). Diameter — 4.5 ft. Launch weight — 28,000 lbs. (A-1); about 30,000 lbs. (A-2); more than 30,000 lbs. (A-3). Guidance — all inertial. Warhead — nuclear. Stages — 2. Propulsion — solid. Total thrust — more than 100,000 lbs.

Principal contractors: Prime — Lockheed. Frame — Lockheed. Guidance — GE, MIT. Fire control — GE. Propulsion — Aerojet (A-1 and the first stage of A-2 and A-3); Hercules (A-2 second stage). Navigation — Sperry Gyroscope, Autonetics. Re-entry vehicle — Lockheed. Launchers — Westinghouse.

History: The Navy started R&D on a seaborne solid-fueled Jupiter in December 1955 and dropped it one year later for Polaris. The first launching of a Polaris from a submerged submarine took place July 20, 1960, off Cape Kennedy. The **George Washington,** first of the Polaris fleet, sailed on her first war patrol November 15, 1960, with 16 operational A-1 Polaris missiles. The A-2 Polaris became operational in 1962, the A-3 in 1964. Navy proposals to deploy Polaris missiles aboard cruisers were rejected several times by both the Eisenhower and Kennedy Administrations. The missile has been offered to the European NATO nations for deployment on land or sea. The total cost of the Polaris R&D program is expected to be 1.9 billion dollars. The total cost of the entire 41-sub program, including R&D, is expected to be about 11 billion dollars. The average cost of 598-class Polaris subs was about 100 million dollars each. The cost of each 616-class sub is 116.2 million dollars. Development of Poseidon, which will carry double the A-3 payload 2,500 miles, was initiated in 1965. It was expected to replace A-2's in 1970.

DEPLOYMENT

Total Polaris submarines authorized through fiscal year 1966: 41.

Total Polaris submarines planned by the Navy: 41.

Missiles per submarine: 16.

Submarines per squadron: 9.

Polaris tenders per squadron: 1.

Location: Deployed through the Atlantic and Pacific Oceans to secret stations within striking distance of Russia. There are three Polaris squadrons in the Atlantic, two in the Pacific.

Polaris Submarines
598 Class

Length — 380 ft. Displacement — 5,600 tons. Crew — 10 officers, 100 men.

U.S.S. George Washington (SSBN 598): Commissioned — 1960. Shipyard — Electric Boat Division, General Dynamics Corp., Groton, Conn.

U.S.S. Patrick Henry (SSBN 599): Commissioned — 1960. Shipyard — Electric Boat.

U.S.S. Theodore Roosevelt (SSBN 600): Commissioned — 1960. Shipyard — U.S. Naval Shipyard, Mare Island, Calif.

U.S.S. Robert E. Lee (SSBN 601): Commissioned — 1960. Shipyard — Newport News Shipbuilding & Drydock Co., Newport News, Va.

U.S.S. Abraham Lincoln (SSBN 602): Commissioned — 1960. Shipyard — U.S. Naval Shipyard, Portsmouth, N.H.

608 Class

Length — 410 ft. Displacement — 6,900 tons. Crew — 10 officers, 100 men.

U.S.S. Ethan Allen (SSBN 608): Commissioned — 1961. Shipyard — Electric Boat.

U.S.S. Sam Houston (SSBN 609): Commissioned — 1962. Shipyard — Newport News.

Polaris A-1 to Poseidon evolution.
—U.S. Navy drawing

Early Polaris.

—U.S. Navy photograph

U.S.S. Thomas A. Edison (SSBN 610): Commissioned — 1962. Shipyard — Electric Boat.

U.S.S. John Marshall (SSBN 611): Commissioned — 1962. Shipyard — Newport News.

U.S.S. Thomas Jefferson (SSBN 618): Commissioned — 1963. Shipyard — Newport News.

616 Class

Length — 425 ft. Displacement — 7,000 tons. Crew — 10 officers, 100 men.

U.S.S. Lafayette (SSBN 616): Commissioned — 1963. Shipyard — Electric Boat.

U.S.S. Alexander Hamilton (SSBN 617): Commissioned — 1963. Shipyard — Electric Boat.

U.S.S. Andrew Jackson (SSBN 619): Commissioned — 1963. Shipyard — Mare Island.

U.S.S. John Adams (SSBN 620): Commissioned — 1963. Shipyard — Portsmouth.

U.S.S. James Monroe (SSBN 622): Commissioned — 1963. Shipyard — Newport News.

U.S.S. Nathan Hale (SSBN 623): Commissioned — 1963. Shipyard — Electric Boat.

U.S.S. Woodrow Wilson (SSBN 624): Commissioned — 1963. Shipyard — Mare Island.

U.S.S. Henry Clay (SSBN 625): Commissioned — 1964. Shipyard — Newport News.

U.S.S. Daniel Webster (SSBN 626): Commissioned — 1964. Shipyard — Electric Boat.

U.S.S. James Madison (SSBN 627): Commissioned — 1964. Shipyard — Newport News.

U.S.S. Tecumseh (SSBN 628): Commissioned — 1964. Shipyard — Electric Boat.

U.S.S. Daniel Boone (SSBN 629): Commissioned — 1964. Shipyard — Mare Island.

U.S.S. John C. Calhoun (SSBN 630): Commissioned — 1964. Shipyard — Newport News.

U.S.S. Ulysses S. Grant (SSBN 631): Commissioned — 1964. Shipyard — Electric Boat.

U.S.S. Von Steuben (SSBN 632): Commissioned — 1964. Shipyard — Newport News.

U.S.S. Casimir Pulaski (SSBN 633): Commissioned — 1964. Shipyard — Electric Boat.

U.S.S. Stonewall Jackson (SSBN 634): Commissioned — 1964. Shipyard — Mare Island.

U.S.S. Sam Rayburn (SSBN 635): Commissioned — 1964. Shipyard — Newport News.

U.S.S. Nathanael Greene (SSBN 636): Commissioned — 1964. Shipyard — Portsmouth.

U.S.S. Benjamin Franklin (SSBN 640): Commissioned — 1965. Shipyard — Electric Boat.

U.S.S. Simon Bolivar (SSBN 641): Commissioned — 1965. Shipyard — Newport News.

U.S.S. Lewis & Clark (SSBN 644): Commissioned 1965. Shipyard — Newport News.

U.S.S. Kamehameha (SSBN 642): Launched — 1965. Shipyard — Mare Island.

U.S.S. George Bancroft (SSBN 643): Launched — 1965. Shipyard — Electric Boat.

U.S.S. James K. Polk (SSBN 645): Launched — 1965. Shipyard — Electric Boat.

U.S.S. George C. Marshall (SSBN 654): Launched — 1965. Shipyard — Newport News.

U.S.S. Henry L. Stimson (SSBN 655): To be launched in 1966. Shipyard — Electric Boat.

U.S.S. George Washington Carver (SSBN 656): To be launched in 1966. Shipyard — Newport News.

U.S.S. Francis Scott Key (SSBN 657): Keel laid — 1964. Shipyard — Electric Boat.

U.S.S. Mariano G. Vallejo (SSBN 658): To be launched in 1966. Shipyard — Mare Island.

U.S.S. Will Rogers (SSBN 659): Keel laid — 1965. Shipyard — Electric Boat.

AIR-LAUNCHED

SRAM — SHORT RANGE ATTACK MISSILE (U.S.)

Type: Air-to-surface.
Military service and designation: Air Force (ZAGM-X-1).
Status: R&D.
Deployment: None.
Performance: Not developed.
Specifications: Not delineated.
Principal contractors: Not announced.
History: Conceived in 1964 as a more obtainable substitute for the 1,000-mile Skybolt ballistic missile scrapped in 1963. SRAM would be designed to supplant Hound Dog missiles on B-52 bombers. It would be ballistic and have a range of about 300 miles. It would be designed mainly to beat down Soviet air defenses, paving the way for a bomber attack.

HOUND DOG (U.S.)

Type: Air-to-surface (air breather).
Military service and designation: Air Force (AGM-28B).
Status: Operational.
Deployment: Location — bases of the Strategic Air Command's B-52H jet bombers in continental United States. Total missiles deployed — about 400. Missiles per B-52H — 2.
Performance: Range — more than 500 nautical miles. Speed — about Mach 2. Ceiling — more than 50,000 ft.
Specifications: Length — 42.5 ft. Diameter — 28 in. Wingspan — 12 ft. Launch weight — about 10,000 lbs. Guidance — inertial. Warhead — nuclear. Propulsion — turbojet (J-52). Total thrust — 7,500 lbs.
Principal contractors: Prime — NAA. Frame — NAA. Guidance — Autonetics. Propulsion — Pratt & Whitney.
History: R&D began in 1957. The Hound Dog was developed from available components as an interim air-to-surface bombardment missile. It gave the Air Force a weapon to help penetrate enemy defenses in heavily defended areas.

KOMET D (U.S.S.R.)

Type: Air-to-surface (air breather).
Military service: Air Force.
Status: Probably operational.
Deployment: Location — intended for strategic (DA) bombers.
Performance: Range — 55 miles.
Specifications: Length — 33.5 ft. Diameter — about 4 ft. Guidance — beam-rider. Warhead — nuclear or HE. Stages — 1. Propulsion — liquid (turbojet).

BLUE STEEL (GREAT BRITAIN)

Type: Air-to-surface (air breather).
Military service: Royal Air Force.
Status: Operational.
Deployment: Location — air launched from British Vulcan bombers.
Performance: Range — about 500 miles. Speed — Mach 12. Ceiling — about 60,000 ft.
Specifications: Length — 36 ft. Wingspan — about 13 ft. Launch weight — about 15,000 lbs. Guidance — inertial. Warhead — nuclear or HE. Stages — 2. Propulsion — liquid.
Principal contractors: Prime — Avro. Guidance — Elliott. Propulsion — Bristol Siddeley.

Quail about to be loaded aboard a B-52.
—General Electric Co. photograph

QUAIL (U.S.)

Type: Air-launched ECM decoy (air breather).
Military service and designation: Air Force (ADM-20C).
Status: Operational.
Deployment: Location — bases of the Strategic Air Command's B-52 jet bombers. Quails are carried inside the bombers.
Performance: Range — more than 200 nautical miles. Speed — near sonic. Ceiling — more than 50,000 ft.
Specifications: Length — 12.9 ft. Wingspan — 5.4 ft. Launch weight — about 1,200 lbs. Guidance — gyro autopilot. Payload — bomber simulation and electronic counter measures (ECM) systems. Propulsion — turbojet (J85-7). Thrust — 2,450 lbs.
Principal contractors: Prime — McDonnell. Frame — McDonnell. Guidance — Summers Gyro. Propulsion — GE. Payload — TRW.
History: R&D began in 1955. Quail became initially operational in 1960. The air-breathing missile serves the dual role of bomber decoy and carrier of ECM systems designed to confuse enemy radar.

Early Lance gets off to successful test flight. Spin devices helping guide the missile emit dark smoke plumes.

5

TACTICAL MISSILES: THE FLEXIBLE SWORD

Mobility and striking power are watchwords of today's armies and navies. This has led to the reshaping of military units the world over around modern aircraft and tactical missiles.

By definition, tactical weapons can be anything short of the multimegaton nuclear warheads delivered by ICBM's and long-range bombers. They include every type of offensive weapon and are equipped with either high-explosive or small nuclear warheads.

Over the years, tactical missiles have been designed for specific purposes: antitank and antipersonnel, antisubmarine, and bombardment. The latter may be missiles launched from aircraft or by land- or sea-based units.

Perhaps the most dramatic change wrought by the missile has been the virtual elimination of heavy artillery by the U.S. Army and Navy. Generals and admirals in the 1960's systematically stripped their combat units of big guns on the theory that missiles offered far greater flexibility and firepower to stop a horde of Russians from sweeping across the plains of Europe. A number of military officials who wondered at the wisdom of this have since become convinced that conventional artillery was abandoned too soon.

No one questions that one of the U.S. Army's big Pershing missiles carrying a large nuclear warhead would be far more effective than whole companies of artillery hammering at targets for days

with high explosives.

The catch is the nuclear warhead. No one would dream of putting a high-explosive warhead on a Pershing to take a shot at a small concentration of guerrillas in the jungle. Each Pershing costs about one million dollars.

The U.S. Army was aware of this drawback in the late 1950's when it began the development of a whole family of short-range bombardment missiles: Honest John, Little John, Sergeant, Shillelagh and, more recently, the Lance. It was seeking low-cost, extremely accurate weapons that could deliver high-explosive warheads ranging in size up to 1,500 pounds anywhere from one to 400 miles. Time has proven, however, that accuracy cannot be obtained at low cost.

The difficulty lies in the solid-propellant fuel employed by the missiles. Even with the most exacting manufacturing standards, military commanders have discovered, a stack of identical-looking solid-fueled missiles cannot be made to burn uniformly. They lack the high degree of "repeatability" characteristic of gunpowder charges employed by artillery. Hence, the missiles must be given "brains" — electronic guidance packages — that double or triple their cost.

Nowhere was the problem more acute than with the U.S. Navy, which had scrapped its 16-inch guns, expecting to replace them with a cheap bombardment missile. Originally, the Navy hoped to adapt to shipboard the Army's Little John, which has a range of 10 miles, to provide battlefield support for the Marines. One Little John cost about $15,000 — about 10 times the price of a World War II 16-inch shell. But the Little Johns were aimed, not guided electronically, and they lacked repeatability. When the Navy investigated equipping Little Johns with even the most inexpensive guidance units, it found the total cost per missile would soar to about $40,000. Too expensive.

For this reason the Navy found itself in the mid-1960's with neither guns nor shipboard bombardment missiles. It had to rely solely on bomber aircraft, a reliance that proved costly in men and planes shot down over Vietnam.

The war against the shadowy Viet Cong revealed a number of limitations in the great array of modern tactical missiles which the United States had developed at a cost of billions of dollars. For example, the Navy-Air Force Bullpup, the services' primary air-to-surface bombardment missile, turned out to be rather ineffective during rainy seasons. The weapon can carry a 250-lb. or 1,000-lb. conventional warhead and is radio guided by the pilot of the launching aircraft. But when low-hanging clouds obscured the target, pilots were unable to use it. This was unfortunate. It meant the pilots were unable to take advantage of the Bullpup's six- to nine-mile range and stay out of antiaircraft fire. Tactical commanders also were reluctant to order use of the Bullpup against small targets because of its relatively high unit cost of about $10,000.

Such deficiencies were attributable to the salient fact that most of America's tactical missiles were really intended to carry nuclear warheads and designed to combat a large-scale military aggression by the Soviet Union. From all indications, the Soviets were in the same predicament. They developed the same type of tactical missiles as the United States and probably would have found themselves even less well equipped for a jungle war.

The special problems associated with tactical missiles have not dampened the enthusiasm of their developers, or of military commanders. They believe the advantages can be exploited with time, and already have been in some cases.

One is the antitank missile. Almost every industrialized nation has built them. France has been in the forefront with the SS-11 and Entac, both produced in large numbers for the U.S. Army.

Most are guided by their operator by means of electrical impulses sent over a hair-thin wire that is payed out as the missile speeds toward its target. Some use other means. None is considered a final satisfactory solution, although several are highly effective.

In recent years, a number of these antitank missiles have been adapted for launching from helicopters and small, light planes, not only against tanks, but against other targets such as pillboxes. This has been a forerunner of a build-up of U.S. Army close-support aircraft armed with improved missiles and free-flight rockets.

The Army has established armed combat reconnaissance aircraft units. Today these include helicopters carrying machine guns and possibly as many as six SS-11's.

Another wide-open field in tactical missile development is ASW — antisubmarine warfare. The United States has already deployed the Asroc surface-to-underwater missile, which is effective up to about 10 miles at most. The much more advanced underwater-to-underwater Subroc, costing $350,000 apiece and with a 30-mile range, joined the fleet starting in 1965. But ASW experts see the need for even greater advances. The Navy would like to be able to reach out 100 or more miles and even farther to strike at enemy submarines prowling beneath the ocean surface.

The essential problem here is not so much the missile as the detection and identification systems. Despite billions of dollars that have been spent on ASW by many nations, the submerged submarine — particularly the nuclear-powered submarine — remains a highly invulnerable target. But many advances in underwater surveillance appear in the making. With them will come the growing need for ASW missiles of great range and accuracy.

Another relatively unfulfilled need for new tactical missiles is in the field of chemical and biological warfare. United States intelligence reports show that Soviet front-line troops today have about one-sixth of their armaments in the form of chemical and biological weapons.

Missiles are excellent carriers of chemical warheads. High-speed drones are another. However, little work has been done by the United States in this area until fairly recently. The only known United States missile designed for chemical warfare is the Army's M-55 — a small, short-range rocket fired from 45-tube launchers to lay down a barrage. But a number of proposals are under consideration, including the modification of existing missiles for chemical warfare.

Probably one of the most revolutionary tactical missile programs in the early 1960's was the development of the nuclear-tipped Davy Crockett, the U.S. Army's new light surface-to-surface missile that makes giant killers out of any team of two GI's. Crockett's sub-kiloton warhead shatters all previous ideas of firepower from small units.

Another aspect of Crockett is its low development and production cost. The missile was created mostly in Army arsenals for less than 2 million dollars.

Crockett symbolizes the key element that is being sought with increasing success in all tactical missiles: great mobility. Two men can carry the lighter version of Crockett on their backs. A jeep can carry the heavy model used to achieve longer range.

Pershing, the U.S. Army's biggest missile punch, is transportable in the field on a tracked vehicle. All other systems, such as power supply and fire control, associated with Pershing can be transported in three other tracked vehicles. The entire system can be moved by helicopter. Even this is not ideal, but it is a long way from the crawling mobility possible only a few years ago with the Redstone, which Pershing replaces. And there is no comparison at all between Pershing and what was possible in World War II. A freight train would have been needed to move an equivalent amount of artillery.

The Army's new Sergeant is deployed on a highly mobile wheeled transporter-erector. The Little John, Honest John, and Shillelagh are all easily transported on relatively light wheeled or tracked vehicles.

This kind of mobility is an old story in Russia. Almost all of the Soviet tactical missiles are mounted on tracked vehicles and have been for a considerable time. That familiar stand-by of May Day parades, the Russian Frog, an equivalent of the Honest John, has been rumbling past reviewing stands in Red Square for years on its armored, tracked carrier. The American move to tracks is late.

But so is deployment with American troops of tactical missiles that have been developed. Over the years, Army missile procurement has been starved for funds. The small number of new missiles in the field is the inevitable result.

The Navy and Air Force have fared better.

The Air Force is buying large quantities of Bullpups with both high-explosive and nuclear warheads. The Air Force also has deployed two squadrons of 650- to 1,200-mile-range Mace missiles in Germany and two in the Far East.

The Navy has deployed sizeable quantities of Bullpups with its carrier air units. The nuclear-tipped Talos, an air defense missile which can be used for shore or surface bombardment, is deployed aboard four cruisers, including the great nuclear-powered *Long Beach*. The Asroc is being placed aboard 150 destroyers, frigates, and cruisers. And the Subroc will be standard armament aboard all hunter-killer submarines.

A similar pattern, in a greater or lesser degree, is found among all major countries on both sides of the Iron Curtain. The rifle, the cannon, and the mortar are still around, but the tactical missile is assuming the central role in tactical weaponry.

SURFACE-TO-SURFACE MISSILES

Pershing launched from its tracked carrier.
—Martin Co. photograph

PERSHING (U.S.)

Type: Surface-to-surface.
Military service and designation: Army (MGM-31A).
Status: Operational.

Deployment: Location — U.S. forces in Europe. Pershing replaced the Redstone. West German forces also have been equipped with Pershings.

Performance: Range — 350 nautical miles. Speed — supersonic.

Specifications: Length — 34 ft. Diameter — 40 in. Launch weight — not available. Guidance — inertial. Warhead — nuclear. Propulsion — solid. Stages — 2.

Principal contractors: Prime — Martin. Frame — Martin. Guidance — Bendix. Propulsion — Thiokol. Transporter-erector-launcher — TRW.

History: Pershing is the U.S. Army's biggest missile. It was designed to succeed the obsolescent Redstone. R&D began in 1958. Pershing became operational in 1964. It is considered highly mobile for a missile of its size. Pershing's range could be extended up to 1,000 miles.

SKEAN* (U.S.S.R.)

Type: Surface-to-surface.

Military service: Army.

Status: Operational.

Deployment: Europe and continental Russia.

Performance: Range — about 1,500 miles. Speed — 13,000 m.p.h.

Specifications: Length — 82 ft. Diameter — 7.5 ft. Launch weight — about 90,000 lbs. Thrust — about 140,000 lbs. Propulsion — liquid. Guidance — inertial. Stages — 1. Warhead — HE or nuclear.

History: Largest and most recently unveiled of three medium-range liquid-fueled ballistic missiles.

*NATO designation.

SANDAL* (U.S.S.R.)

Type: Surface-to-surface.

Military service: Army.

Status: Operational.

Deployment: Europe and continental Russia.

Performance: Range — about 1,100 miles. Speed — 13,000 m.p.h.

Specifications: Length — 73 ft. Diameter — 5 ft. Launch weight — about 57,000 lbs. Thrust — about 100,000 lbs. Guidance — inertial. Warhead — HE or nuclear. Stages — 1. Propulsion — liquid.

History: Developed, as was the United States Redstone, from the German V-2. It was deployed briefly in Cuba in 1962, precipitating the crisis between the U.S. and the U.S.S.R.

* NATO designation.

SHYSTER* (U.S.S.R.)

Type: Surface-to-surface.

Military service: Army.

Status: Operational.

Shyster, 1965.
—Novosti Press Agency photograph

Deployment: Europe and continental Russia.

Performance: Range — about 600 miles. Speed — 10,000 m.p.h.

Specifications: Length — 69 ft. Diameter — 4.5 ft. Launch weight — about 50,000 lbs. Thrust — about 85,000 lbs. Propulsion — liquid. Guidance — inertial. Stages — 1. Warhead — HE or nuclear.

History: Smallest of the Skean, Sandal, Shyster family, this missile apparently has undergone improvements and updating over the years. It is due for replacement by a solid-fueled model.

*NATO designation.

CRUISE MISSILE (U.S.S.R.)

Type: Surface-to-surface (air breather).

Military service: Navy and Army.

Status: Operational.

Deployment: Location — with Red Army combat units and aboard at least 7 cruisers.

Performance: Range — 450 to 600 miles. Speed — supersonic.

Specifications: Length — 36 ft. Wingspan — unavailable. Guidance — beam-rider or programed. Warhead — nuclear or HE. Stages — 2. Propulsion — cluster of 4 solid-fueled booster rockets, liquid ramjet sustainer. It was deployed briefly in Cuba in 1962.

Iron Maiden.
—Novosti Press Agency photograph

IRON MAIDEN (U.S.S.R.)

Type: Mobile surface-to-surface.

Military service: Army.

Status: Operational.

Deployment: Red Army combat units.

Performance: Range — up to 400 miles. Speed — 3,000 m.p.h.

Specifications: Not disclosed. Propulsion apparently is solid, and the rocket probably is radio guided. Launch is from tracked carrier.

History: First unveiled in 1965.

MACE (U.S.)

Type: Surface-to-surface (air breather).

Military service and designation: Air Force (CGM-13B).

Status: Operational.

Deployment: Location — United States troops in West Germany and on Okinawa. Divisional strength — about 50 missiles. (West Germany planned to buy Maces but switched to Pershings.)

Performance: Range — more than 650 nautical miles (A); more than 1,200 nautical miles (B). Speed — more than 650 m.p.h. (A); more than 650 m.p.h. and supersonic in terminal dive (B). Ceiling — more than 40,000 ft.

Specifications: Length — 44 ft. Diameter — 54 in. Wingspan — 22.9 ft. Launch weight — 15,500 lbs. Guidance — ATRAN map matching (A); inertial (B). Warhead — nuclear or HE. Propulsion — solid (first stage); J-33-41 turbojet (second stage). Stages — 2. Thrust — 100,000 lbs. (first stage); 5,200 lbs. (second stage).

Principal contractors: Prime — Martin. Frame — Martin. Guidance — Goodyear (A); AC Spark Plug (B). Propulsion — Thiokol (first stage); Allison (second stage). Launcher — Goodyear (A); Martin (B).

History: R&D began in 1953. Mace became operational in 1961. The missile replaced the Matador. It is deployed in both soft and hardened sites.

SERGEANT (U.S.)

Type: Surface-to-surface.

Military service and designation: Army (MGM-29A).

Status: Operational.

Deployment: Location — replaced the unguided Corporal with Army units in continental United States and Europe.

Performance: Range — 85 miles. Speed — supersonic.

Specifications: Length — 35 ft. Diameter — 31 in. Launch weight — 10,000 lbs. Guidance — inertial. Warhead — nuclear or HE. Propulsion — solid. Stages — 1. Thrust — about 55,000 lbs.

Principal contractors: Prime — Sperry Utah. Frame — Sperry. Guidance — Sperry. Propulsion — Thiokol. Launcher — LTV.

Sergeant flies from White Sands, N. M., test range.
—Sperry Co. photograph

History: R&D began in 1955. Sergeant became initially operational in 1961. It was offered to European NATO nations after the 1962 scrapping of the British Blue Water.

AL KAHER (EGYPT)

Type: Surface-to-surface.

Military service: Army.

Status: Production.

Deployment: With Army units of the United Arab Republic along the southwest border of Israel.

Performance: Range — more than 300 miles. Speed — about 3,000 m.p.h.

Specifications: Length — about 40 ft. Tailspan — 10.5 ft. Diameter — 4.5 ft. Stages — 1. Propulsion — liquid. Guidance — autopilot. Warhead — 2,000 lbs. HE.

History: Development started in secrecy in late 1950's by West German rocket scientists imported by

Premier Nasser. The missile was unveiled in July 1962 along with a smaller version, the Al Zafer. It is designed for bombardment and not considered very accurate. Al Kaher means "The Conqueror."

AL ZAFER (EGYPT)

Type: Surface-to-surface.

Military service: Army.

Status: Production.

Deployment: With Army units of the United Arab Republic along southwest border of Israel.

Performance: Range — more than 200 miles. Speed — about 3,000 m.p.h.

Specifications: Length — about 30 ft. Tailspan — 8 ft. Diameter — 4 ft. Stages — 1. Propulsion — liquid. Guidance — autopilot. Warhead — 1,500 lbs. HE.

History: Developed along with Al Kaher. Design is quite similar to the old German V-2. Al Zafer means "The Winner." The Egyptians were reported to be developing a 600-mile-range, two-stage missile of higher accuracy.

SCUD* (U.S.S.R.)

Type: Surface-to-surface.

Military service: Army.

Status: Operational.

Deployment: Location — Red Army combat units.

Performance: Range — 50 to 90 miles. Speed — Mach 5.

Specifications: Length — 30 ft. Diameter — 2.5 ft. Launch weight — about 10,000 lbs. Guidance — radio command. Warhead — HE. Stages — 2. Propulsion — solid.

* NATO designation.

Shavit II.

SHAVIT II (ISRAEL)

Type: Surface-to-surface.

Military service: Army.

Status: R&D.

Deployment: None.

Performance: Range — about 70 miles. Speed — about Mach 5.

Specifications: Length — about 20 ft. Tailspan — about 4.5 ft. Launch weight — 550 lbs. Guidance — unavailable. Warhead — HE and possibly nuclear. Stages — 2. Propulsion — all solid.

Principal contractor: Israeli government's Military Industries.

History: Program has been kept highly secret in view of missile build-up by Egyptians.

Robot 315.

ROBOT 315 (SWEDEN)

Type: Surface-to-surface (air breather).

Military service: Navy.

Status: Operational.

Deployment: Location — installations on the Swedish destroyers **Smaland** and **Holland**.

Performance: Range — up to 20 nautical miles. Speed — Mach .9.

Specifications: Length — 24 ft. Wingspan — 8 ft. Launch weight — about 3,000 lbs. Guidance — radio command. Warhead — HE. Stages — 2. Propulsion — solid booster and pulse-jet sustainer.

Principal contractor: Robotbyran.

FROG-1* (U.S.S.R.)

Type: Surface-to-surface.

Military service: Army.

Status: Operational (but being phased out).

Deployment: Location — Red Army units. Deployed aboard tracked vehicles.

Performance: Range — 15 to 25 miles.

Specifications: Length — 31 ft. Diameter — 2 ft. Finspan — 3 ft. Weight — about 6,000 lbs. Guidance — free flight. Warhead — HE and possibly nuclear. Stages — 1. Propulsion — solid.

* NATO designation.

Shillelagh launched from tank cannon.
—U.S. Army photograph

SHILLELAGH (U.S.)

Type: Surface-to-surface.

Military service and designation: Army (XMGM-51A).

Status: Production.

Deployment: Location — to be deployed with combat units for close-in heavy support. It is mounted on tanks and fired from 152-mm. gun launchers.

Specifications: Length — not disclosed. Diameter — 6 in. Stages — 1. Propulsion — solid. Guidance — Command/IR.

Principal contractors: Prime — Aeronutronic. Fire control — Raytheon.

History: R&D began in 1958.

LANCE (U.S.)

Type: Surface-to-surface.

Military service and designation: Army (XMGM-52A).

Status: Development.

Performance: Range — up to 25 miles. Speed — supersonic.

Specifications: Length — about 20 ft. Diameter — 22 in. Weight — 3,200 lbs. Stages — 1. Propulsion — liquid (prepackaged storable). Guidance — simplified inertial. Warhead — HE or nuclear.

Principal contractors: Prime — LTV. Propulsion — Rocketdyne. Guidance — LTV, Systron-Donner, Bosch-Arma. Launch vehicle — FMC.

Lance model on tracked launcher.
—U.S. Army photograph

History: Formerly designated "Missile B," R&D was initiated in 1960 and development began in 1962. Lance was intended as a replacement for the unguided Little John and Honest John battlefield support weapons.

Honest John with U.S. and Italian troops in Italy.
—U.S. Army photograph

HONEST JOHN (U.S.)

Type: Surface-to-surface.

Military service and designation: Army (MGR-1B).

Status: Operational.

Deployment: Location — United States forces in continental United States, Europe, and Far East. Also in the hands of NATO allies. Battalion strength — four launchers.

Performance: Range — 12 miles. Speed — Mach 1.7.

Specifications: Length — 27 ft. Diameter — 30 in. Launch weight — 5,800 lbs. Guidance — free flight. Warhead — nuclear or HE. Propulsion — solid. Stages — 1 plus spin rockets.

Principal contractors: Prime — Douglas. Frame — Douglas, Emerson Electric. Propulsion — Emerson Electric (booster); Thiokol (spin rockets).

History: Honest John is currently the mainstay tactical missile of the U.S. Army. R&D began in 1951. Honest John became initially operational in 1953.

Little John.

—U.S. Army photograph

LITTLE JOHN (U.S.)

Type: Surface-to-surface.

Military service and designation: Army (MGR-3A).

Status: Operational.

Deployment: Location — Army units in continental United States and Europe.

Performance: Range — 10 nautical miles. Speed — supersonic.

Specifications: Length — 14 ft. 5 in. Diameter — 12.5 in. Launch weight — 780 lbs. Guidance — free flight. Warhead — nuclear or HE. Propulsion — solid. Stages — 1.

Principal contractors: Prime — Emerson Electric. Frame — Emerson Electric. Propulsion — Hercules.

History: R&D began in 1955. Little John became initially operational in 1960. It is a highly mobile missile that can be airlifted easily.

Soviet chemical troops man Frog-2.

—Tass photograph

FROG-2* (U.S.S.R.)

Type: Surface-to-surface.

Military service: Army.

Status: Operational since 1957.

Deployment: Location — with Red Army units aboard tracked vehicles.

Performance: Range — about 10 miles.

Specifications: Length — about 29 ft. Diameter — 1 ft. Weight — about 4,000 lbs. Finspan — about 3 ft. Guidance — free flight. Warhead — HE or nuclear. Stages — 1. Propulsion — solid.

* NATO designation.

FROG-4* (U.S.S.R.)

Type: Surface-to-surface.

Military service: Army.

Status: Operational.

Deployment: Location — with Red Army combat units in western Russia and eastern Europe; fired from tank launchers.

Performance: Range — 50 miles.

Specifications: Length — about 35 ft. Launch weight — 4,000 lbs. Guidance — unavailable. Warhead — HE or nuclear. Stages — 2. Propulsion — all solid.

* NATO designation.

AIRONE (ITALY)

Type: Surface-to-surface.

Military service: Army.

Status: Operational.

Deployment: Location — Italian Army combat units.

Performance: Range — 6 miles.

Specifications: Solid-fueled, free-flight rocket carrying HE or other types of conventional warheads. Fired in salvos.

DAVY CROCKETT (U.S.)

Type: Surface-to-surface.

Military service and designation: Army (MGM-51A).

Status: Operational.

Davy Crockett.
—U.S. Army photograph

M-55.
—U.S. Army photograph

Deployment: Location — to be deployed widely with United States combat units.

Performance: Range — relatively short. Range can be varied by launching from long- (M-29) and short-range (M-28) launchers.

Specifications: Length — about 4 ft. Warhead — nuclear (sub-kiloton). Propulsion — solid. Stages — 1.

Principal contractor: Army Weapons Command.

History: R&D began in late 1956. Davy Crockett became initially operational in 1961. It is the first United States nuclear weapon that can be carried and launched by only two infantrymen. The larger launcher, the M-29, is mounted on jeeps and other vehicles. Davy Crockett is considered to be the forerunner of the small tactical missile tipped with a nuclear warhead.

M-55 (U.S.)

Type: Surface-to-surface.

Military service: Army.

Status: Operational.

Deployment: Location — units of combat-ready divisions in the continental United States and Europe.

Performance: Range — relatively short. (Missiles are launched in salvos from a 45-tube T-145 launcher.) Guidance — free flight. Warhead — HE or chemical agents.

Principal contractor: Prime — Norris Thermador.

History: R&D began about 1957. M-55 became initially operational in 1960. It is the Army's first missile designed primarily for the delivery of chemical agents.

GVAI's.

GVAI (U.S.S.R.)

Type: Surface-to-surface.

Military service: Army.

Status: Operational, but probably replaced by more advanced type of barrage rocket.

Performance: Range — short. Fired from multiple launcher. No other details available.

ANTITANK MISSILES

TOW.
—Hughes Aircraft Co. photograph

TOW (U.S.)

Type: Surface-to-surface.

Military service: Army.

Status: Development.

Performance: Range — up to 5 miles. Speed — supersonic.

Specifications: Length — about 4 ft. Diameter — 6 in. Weight — not disclosed. Guidance — optically tracked and guided by radio wire command link. Warhead — HE. Propulsion — solid.

Principal contractors: Prime — Hughes. Propulsion — Hercules.

History: Development started in 1963 to provide infantrymen with heavy assault weapon able to demolish tanks and fortifications. Designed for transport by troops on foot or by M-113 personnel carrier.

Cobra.
—U.S. Marine Corps photograph

COBRA (WEST GERMANY)

Type: Surface-to-surface.

Military service: Army.

Status: Operational.

Deployment: Location — with units of the West German Army, also in continental United States with Marine Corps evaluation units.

Performance: Range — 5,940 ft. (max.); 5,280 ft. (effective). Speed — 191 m.p.h.

Specifications: Length — 30.7 in. Diameter — 3.9 in. Height — 13.6 in. Wingspan — 19 in. Launch weight — 20.2 lbs. Guidance — wire. Warhead — HE. Propulsion — solid. Stages — 1.

Principal contractors: Prime — Boelkow. (U.S. distributor — Daystrom.) Frame — Boelkow. Guidance — Boelkow. Propulsion — Oerlikon.

History: Cobra is the first German post-World War II missile of note. R&D began in 1957. Cobra became initially operational in 1960. NATO has considered adopting it.

SS-10 (FRANCE)

Type: Surface-to-surface and air-to-surface.

Military service: Army.

Status: Operational.

Deployment: Location — widely used by NATO armies in Europe. U.S. Army procured a sizeable number, but has switched to Entac. SS-10's are used by infantry, armored and helicopter units.

Performance: Range — 5,250 ft. (effective). Speed — 180 m.p.h.

Specifications: Length — 34 in. Diameter — 6 in. Wingspan — 30 in. Launch weight — 33 lbs. Guidance — wire. Warhead — HE. Propulsion — solid. Stages — 1.

Principal contractors: Prime — Nord. (GE is U.S. licensee.) Frame — Nord. Guidance — Nord. Propulsion — Nord.

History: SS-10 is one of the world's most widely known and deployed antitank missiles. R&D began in 1950. SS-10 became initially operational in 1956. SS-10's have been used in battle by the French and Israeli armies.

SS-11 (FRANCE)

Type: Surface-to-surface and air-to-surface.

Military service: Army.

Status: Operational.

Deployment: Location — in Europe with French and other NATO forces, in continental United States with U.S. Army units. The U.S. Army deploys S-11's on vehicles and helicopters.

Performance: Range — 1,650 to 11,500 ft. (effective). Speed — more than 400 m.p.h.

Specifications: Length — 46 in. Diameter — 6 in. Wingspan — 20 in. Launch weight — 62 lbs. Guidance

SS-11 launched from armored personnel carrier.
—U.S. Army photograph

— wire. Warhead — HE. Propulsion — solid. Stages
— 1.

Principal contractors: Prime — Nord. (GE is U.S. licensee.) Frame — Nord. Guidance — Nord. Propulsion — Nord.

History: SS-11 is an advanced, heavier version of the
SS-10. Because of its size and weight, it is gen-
really considered to be best employed when
launched from vehicles or aircraft. R&D began in
1954. SS-11 became initially operational in 1960.

Vigilants.
—Vickers-Armstrongs, Ltd., photograph

VIGILANT (GREAT BRITAIN)

Type: Surface-to-surface.

Military service: Army.

Status: Operational.

Deployment: British infantry units.

Performance: Range — 200 to 1,700 yards. Speed —
350 m.p.h.

Specifications: Length — 3 ft. Diameter — 4.5 in.
Launch weight — about 26 lbs. Guidance — wire,
with gyro autopilot. Warhead — HE. Stages — 1.
Propulsion — solid.

Principal contractor: Prime — Vickers.

BANTAM (SWEDEN)

Type: Surface-to-surface.

Military service: Army.

Status: Operational.

Deployment: Location — with Swedish Army combat
troops (can be fired from the hip).

Performance: Range — 6,500 ft. Speed — 190 m.p.h.

Specifications: Length — 2.5 ft. Launch weight — 13
lbs. Guidance — wire. Warhead — HE. Stages — 2.
Propulsion — all solid.

Principal contractor: Bofors.

MALKARA (AUSTRALIA)

Type: Surface-to-surface.

Military service: Army.

Status: Operational.

Deployment: Location — Australian and British combat
troops. (Note: the Malkara has been demonstrated
to be highly effective against bunker fortifications
as well as tanks.)

Performance: Range — about 2 miles. Speed — subsonic.

Specifications: Length — 6.5 ft. Wingspan — 2.5 ft.
Launch weight — 206 lbs. Guidance — wire. Warhead — HE. Stages — 2. Propulsion — all solid.

Principal contractor: Government Aircraft Factories.

MOSQUITO (SWITZERLAND)

Type: Surface-to-surface.

Military service: Army.

Status: Operational.

Deployment: Location — Swiss Army units.

Performance: Range — about 6,200 ft. Speed — 200
m.p.h.

Specifications: Length — 3 ft. Launch weight — 23 lbs.
Guidance — wire. Warhead — HE. Stages — 2.
Propulsion — all solid.

Principal contractor: Prime — Contraves.

Entacs on U.S. Army jeep.
—U.S. Army photograph

ENTAC (FRANCE)

Type: Surface-to-surface.

Military service: Army (U.S. designation MGM-32A).

Status: Operational.

Deployment: Being purchased for infantry units by the United States and Belgium. Deployment started in 1962.

Performance: Range — about 1 mile. Speed — about 180 m.p.h.

Specifications: Launch weight — 37 lbs. Guidance — wire. Warhead — HE. Stages — 1. Propulsion — solid.

History: Developed by Nord Aviation and French Defense Agency with large financial support from U.S. Army.

SS-12 (FRANCE)

Type: Surface-to-surface and air-to-surface.

Military service: Army.

Status: Awaiting production.

Deployment: Location — intended for French Army combat troops; also can be launched from light aircraft and helicopters and used for coastal defense.

Performance: Range — more than 4 miles. Speed — Mach 1.

Specifications: Frame — about 6 ft. Wingspan — about 32 in. Launch weight — 150 lbs. Guidance — wire, also alternate radar version. Warhead — nuclear or HE. Stages — 1. Propulsion — solid.

Principal contractor: Nord.

History: R&D was completed in mid-1961. The SS-12 is an advanced version of the SS-11.

TATM-1 (JAPAN)

Type: Surface-to-surface.

Military service: Army.

Status: R&D.

Deployment: None.

Performance: Not available.

Specifications: Length — 4.5 ft. Launch weight — 300 lbs. (A 3.2-ft.-long model TATM-2 also is under development as an antitank weapon.)

Principal contractor: Kawasaki.

SNAPPER* (U.S.S.R.)

Type: Surface-to-surface.

Military service: Army.

Status: Operational.

Deployment: With mobile Red Army units.

Performance: Range — 1.5 miles.

Specifications: Length — about 3.5 ft. Diameter — 4 in. Weight — not disclosed. Guidance — wire-command. Propulsion — solid. Warhead — HE.

* NATO designation.

Snappers in the field.

—Tass photograph

PSR-1 (ARGENTINA)

Type: Surface-to-surface.

Military service: Army.

Status: R&D.

Deployment: Location — intended for infantry units. PSR-1 is shoulder-fired like United States World War II bazooka.

Performance: Range — short.

Specifications: Length — 3.8 ft. Launch weight — 19.5 lbs. Guidance — free flight. Warhead — HE. Stages — 1. Propulsion — solid.

AIR-TO-SURFACE MISSILES

Bullpup fired from Marine helicopter.

—U.S. Navy photograph

BULLPUP (U.S.)

Type: Air-to-surface.

Military service and designation: Navy (AGM-12B, C) and Air Force (AGM-12D).

Status: Operational.

Deployment: Location — widely deployed on carrier-based aircraft, and in air units of the Marine Corps and Air Force in continental United States and overseas.

Performance: Range — 3 to 6 nautical miles. Speed — Mach 1.8.

Specifications: Length — 11 ft. Diameter — about 1 ft. Launch weight — 571 lbs. Guidance — radio command with visual reference. Warhead — HE and nuclear. The HE warhead varies from 250 to 1,000 lbs. Propulsion — solid and packaged liquid.

Principal contractors: Prime — Martin; Maxson (second source). Frame — Martin. Guidance — Martin. Propulsion — Allegany (solid); Thiokol (packaged liquid).

History: R&D began in 1953. Bullpup became initially operational aboard the carrier **Lexington** in 1959. The Navy models have HE warheads; the Air Force model has a nuclear warhead and HE. NATO models are produced in Norway.

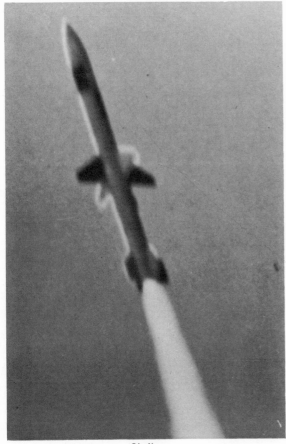

Shrike.

—U. S. Navy photograph

SHRIKE (U.S.)

Type: Air-to-surface (antiradar).

Military service and designation: Navy (AGM-45A).

Status: Operational.

Performance: Range — about 12 miles. Speed — 3,000 m.p.h.

Specifications: Length — 14 ft. Diameter — 9 in. Weight 420 lbs. Guidance — radar homing. Stages — 1. Propulsion — liquid (prepackaged storable.) Warhead — HE.

Principal contractors: Prime — NOTS. Guidance — Texas Instruments. Propulsion — Rocketdyne.

History: Developed from the Sparrow air-to-air missile; designed for combatting Soviet radar-guided anti-aircraft missiles. It homes in on radar beacons emanating from missile batteries.

AS 30 (FRANCE)

Type: Air-to-surface.

Military service: Navy and Air Force.

Status: Operational.

Deployment: With French and British air units.

Performance: Range — almost 9 miles. Speed — supersonic.

Specifications: Length — 12.4 ft. Diameter — 13.8 in. Wingspan — 3.3 ft. Launch weight — 1,100 lbs. Guidance — proportional control. Warhead — HE. Stages — 2. Propulsion — solid.

Principal contractor: Prime — Nord.

History: Unveiled in 1961, AS 30 was offered to NATO countries as a competitor to the United States Bullpup and lost. The AS 20 is a smaller version with a 3-mile range.

ZUNI (U.S.)

Type: Air-to-surface.

Military service and designation: Navy (MK-40).

Status: Operational.

Deployment: Location — carrier-based aircraft.

Performance: Range — about 5 nautical miles. Speed — about Mach 2 plus.

Specifications: Length — 9 ft. 2 in. Diameter — 5 in. Launch weight — 107 lbs. Guidance — free flight. Warhead — HE or flares. Propulsion — solid. Stages — 1. Thrust — 7,000 lbs.

Principal contractor: Prime — NOTS.

History: NOTS began development of the Zuni in 1955. The missile first became operational in 1957. Zuni launchers, which also are used for storing and transporting the missiles, can be jettisoned from planes after the missiles are launched. AD-type Navy aircraft can carry as many as 48 Zuni missiles.

Robot 304.

ROBOT 304 (SWEDEN)

Type: Air-to-surface.

Military service: Air Force.

Status: Operational.

Deployment: Aboard Swedish Air Force fighters.

Performance: Range — about 3 miles. Speed — Mach 1.

Specifications: Length — 14.5 ft. Wingspan — 6.6 in. Launch weight — 1,000 lbs. Guidance — radio command. Warhead — HE. Stages — 1. Propulsion — solid.

Principal contractor: Robotbyran.

History: R&D began in 1950. First production model was launched from a Saab J-29 fighter in 1955.

PAT-1.

PAT-1 (ARGENTINA)

Type: Air-to-surface.

Military service: Air Force.

Status: R&D.

Deployment: Location — intended for attack bombers.

Performance: Range — about 12 miles. Speed — subsonic.

Specifications: Length — about 11 ft. Diameter — about 1 ft. Launch weight — 2,310 lbs. Guidance — not specified. Warhead — HE. Stages — 1. Propulsion — liquid.

Principal contractor: Fabrica Militar.

ANTISUBMARINE WARFARE (ASW) MISSILES

Alfa.

—U.S. Navy photograph

WEAPON ALFA (U.S.)

Type: ASW surface-to-underwater.

Military service and designation: Navy (RUR-4).

Status: Operational.

Deployment: Location — aboard destroyer escorts and frigates.

Performance: Range — about 900 yards.

Specifications: Length — 8.5 ft. Diameter — 12.75 in. Launch weight — 500 lbs. Guidance — free flight. Warhead — HE. Propulsion — solid. Stages — 1. (Alfa is launched from guns mounted in turrets.)

Principal contractors: Prime — Navy. Frame — Avco.

History: R&D began in 1946. Alfa became initially operational in 1952. It is now far outclassed by Asroc and is made virtually obsolescent by nuclear-powered submarines.

MALAFON (FRANCE)

Type: Surface-to-underwater.

Military service: Navy.

Status: Operational.

Deployment: Location — first installations were aboard the 3,750-ton ASW command ship **La Galissonière** in 1962.

Performance: Range — more than 10 nautical miles.

Specifications: Length — about 22 ft. Wingspan — 12 ft. Guidance — sonar/radio command. Warhead — HE homing torpedo. Stages — 2. Propulsion — solid booster.

Principal contractor: SIAL.

Subroc launching from submarine.
—U.S. Navy photograph

SUBROC (U.S.)

Type: ASW underwater-to-underwater via air.

Military service and designation: Navy (UUM-44A).

Status: Operational.

Deployment: Location — aboard nuclear-powered hunter-killer submarines.

Performance: Range — about 25 nautical miles.

Specifications: Length — 21 ft. Diameter — 21 in. Weight — 4,000 lbs. Guidance — inertial. Stages — 2. Propulsion — solid. Warhead — HE or nuclear.

Principal contractors: Prime — Goodyear. Frame — Goodyear. Guidance — Kearfott. Fire control — Librascope. Propulsion — Thiokol.

History: R&D began in 1958. Subroc became initially operational in 1961. The missile is the most advanced ASW weapon developed to date by the United States. It enables a submarine for the first time to attack another submarine at extended range. Development was delayed by 1963 sinking of **U.S.S. Thresher** when special test gear went down with all hands aboard.

ERIKA (SWEDEN)

Type: ASW surface-to-underwater.

Military service: Navy.

Status: R&D.

Deployment: Location — intended for ASW naval units.

Performance: Range — more than 1 mile at 170-ft. depth.

Specifications: Length — 6.7 ft. Weight — 550 lbs. Guidance — not available. Warhead — HE. Stages — 1. Propulsion — solid.

Principal contractor: Bofors.

TERNE III (NORWAY)

Type: Ship-to-underwater.

Military service: Navy.

Status: Operational.

Deployment: Aboard Norwegian Navy antisubmarine ships in multiple launchers of 6. The United States and other countries have purchased production models for evaluation.

Performance: Range — more than 3.5 miles.

Specifications: Length — 6.5 ft. Diameter — 7.9 in. Guidance — sonar-directed free flight. Warhead — HE (depth charge). Stages — 1. Propulsion — solid.

Principal contractor: Koengsberg.

Asroc.
—U.S. Navy photograph

ASROC (U.S.)

Type: ASW surface-to-underwater.

Military service and designation: Navy (RUR-5A).

Status: Operational.

Deployment: Location — aboard one cruiser, **U.S.S. Long Beach;** one destroyer leader, **U.S.S. Norfolk;** three destroyers, **U.S.S. Perry, U.S.S. C. F. Adams, U.S.S. H. B. Wilson;** and five frigates, **U.S.S. Dewey, U.S.S. Mahan, U.S.S. King, U.S.S. Preble, U.S.S. Farragut.** Future — authorized for 17 more frigates, including the nuclear-powered **U.S.S. Bainbridge.** Asroc is scheduled to be deployed aboard a total of about 150 destroyers and cruisers over the next few years.

Performance: Range — about 8 nautical miles. Speed — about Mach 1.

Specifications: Length — 15 ft. (torpedo warhead alone is 100 in.). Diameter — 2.5 ft. Launch weight — about 1,000 lbs. Guidance — free flight. Warhead — HE or nuclear. Asroc can carry either the HE-tipped Mark 44 acoustic-homing torpedo (MK-3) or a depth charge that can be either HE or nuclear (MK-2). Propulsion — solid. Stages — 1 plus either the torpedo or depth charge. Sonar detection system — SQS-23. Launcher capacity — 8.

Principal contractors: Prime — Minneapolis-Honeywell. Frame — Minneapolis-Honeywell. Fire control — Librascope. Sonar detection system — Sangamo. Torpedo — GE. Launcher — Universal Match.

History: R&D began in 1956. Asroc became initially operational in 1960 aboard the **Norfolk** and **Perry.** The missile was a major improvement over Alfa. One interesting feature is the pepperbox launcher that can fire in almost any direction.

Exterior of superfast Sprint anti-ICBM turns incandescent from air friction as it streaks into space like a comet.

—U. S. Army photograph

6

AEROSPACE DEFENSE:
THE NUCLEAR UMBRELLA

Midway in the 1964 election campaign President Johnson created a small sensation by announcing that the United States had perfected a way of destroying enemy satellites as they cruised in orbit.

Defense Secretary Robert S. McNamara tried to soften the ring of political one-upmanship. (Republicans were charging the Administration with neglecting the Soviet space threat.) He said the system had been tested against American satellites and proven effective with some actual but nondestructive intercepts. It soon became evident, however, that Johnson was talking about a research project — not a true anti-satellite weapon. It consisted of some Thrust Augmented Thor missiles on Johnston Island, 1,000 miles southwest of Hawaii — and a few R&D models of the Nike-Zeus, an anti-ICBM missile, on Kwajalein atoll, also in the Pacific. A similar intercept of a satellite by an air-launched Bold Orion research missile had been performed by the Air Force back in 1960. So not even the concept was new.

The two installations never were established on a combat basis, able to destroy a covey of Soviet orbital bombs on a moment's notice. No pictures were released and virtually all mention of the weapons was subsequently avoided by the Pentagon.

The President's announcement did serve a purpose, however. It diverted attention from a much more worrisome problem: whether the nation should invest 20 billion dollars in an anti-ICBM system to protect most of the population living in cities in the event of nuclear war. Missiles — not orbital bombs — were an immediate threat. But this wasn't debated in the campaign.

On the face of it, it seemed incredible that the United States was not actively deploying anti-missile missiles around the country. That such defensive weapons were possible seemingly had been proven by the 2-billion-dollar Nike-Zeus research program under way since 1957. In 1963, the U.S. Army had announced several Nike-Zeus intercepts of Atlas and Titan mock warheads fired over the Pacific. The Russians claimed they, too, had an anti-ICBM. Moreover, it was widely appreciated that whichever of the great powers first obtained a truly effective anti-ICBM would gain a decisive strategic advantage over the other, for the possessor of such a system would be able to attack the second country with full knowledge that it could not be damaged by retaliatory missiles.

Below the surface, however, there were many complex technical and political reasons for postponing such a monumental defense project. In the first place, military authorities argued that setting up anti-ICBM batteries was foolish unless they were accompanied by construction, also on a nationwide scale, of civilian fallout shelters. They pointed out no anti-ICBM could be made 100 per cent effective; the Russians could merely drop their warheads to the west of populated areas, away from defending missiles, and let the wind carry deadly radioactive debris across farm and city.

But the diplomats contended that a big fallout-shelter program would be interpreted abroad as a sure sign that the United States was preparing to wage war. It would have the effect of escalating the arms race and would raise international tensions — just the opposite of long-standing United States policy to find a peaceful settlement to the Cold War. Besides, there was no indication that the Russians were building shelters.

Congress might have disregarded these arguments and forced action on both the deployment of antimissile missiles and construction of shelters if it had not been for some valid doubts about the technical feasibility of the whole proposition. These doubts were rooted in some highly secret experiments which showed that Nike-Zeus really wasn't the answer. It could stop a single warhead under laboratory conditions. But all-out war would be radically different.

The secret experiments involved firing warheads at Zeus that contained not only a simulated nuclear weapon but a large number of decoys. The decoys, fabricated of metallic balloons and streamers of tinfoil-like "chaff," showed up on the Zeus radar on Kwajalein as so many more warheads spreading out in the sky. It was obvious that the Russians could build warheads similarly equipped and make it virtually impossible to pick out the real one to shoot down. That meant putting dozens of missiles in each Zeus battery to cope with all the incoming targets. But since it was cheap and easy to release a cloud of decoys, it was apparent that any Zeus battery, no matter how big, could be saturated with targets and quickly exhausted.

The decoy experiments did reveal one significant piece of information, however. The decoys looked like warheads only when they were sailing through space. When they started to descend, they were so light that they bounced off the top of the atmosphere, turning upward, while the heavy simulated nuclear weapon bored straight in. Scientists realized that here was a way of discriminating between the two. Unfortunately, the atmosphere only extends up about 250,000 feet or about 50 miles. So it would mean the warhead was right overhead at the moment it could be detected — and traveling at 5 miles per second. There were 10 seconds in which it could be intercepted.

Building an antimissile missile that can react

that fast sounds impossible. But that's what the United States has been trying to do since 1964 with a new project known as Nike-X. And rocketmen have had some success, surprisingly enough.

They have concentrated on the development of a super-powered solid-fueled missile — Sprint — which is popped from a launching tube by compressed gas, much like a Polaris missile, and then literally explodes straight upward. Sprint moves so fast it is out of sight in the blink of an eye.

The project envisions employing Sprint as a booster to whoosh a Nike-X warhead to an altitude of about 10 miles in less than 5 seconds after ground radar locks on an incoming target warhead. The Nike-X would explode a small nuclear device at the 10-mile level to destroy the enemy missile. This would happen far enough up to avoid damage to a city below, in theory and if the timing was right.

There was pressure to proceed with the deployment of Nike-X long in advance of its successful fruition as a weapon. But defense officials refused to be stampeded. The matter of a fallout-shelter program remained; indeed, it was even more necessary now. And a new complication had suddenly appeared: maneuverable warheads.

The science of re-entry physics had brought this about. Scientists had once paled at the idea of ever contriving a warhead that could survive the searing heat of re-entry. Experiments had not only solved the problem but shown researchers how to design warheads of all different sizes and shapes that could skip and dance as they hit the atmosphere — and avoid defense missiles.

More research by the Atomic Energy Commission had further reduced the weight and compressed the size of nuclear bombs while retaining their "bang." So it became possible to make warheads that glided and soared before homing in on a target and, because of the small size, multiple warheads fitting aboard one ICBM that also maneuvered.

This new development — which the Pentagon promptly began to exploit for its advanced Minuteman II ICBM and Poseidon submarine-launched missiles — once again made the whole problem of missile defense virtually impossible. The Russians undoubtedly would obtain multiple maneuverable warheads. They also knew about decoys. It raised the specter of the skies literally being filled with nuclear death in the event of war. Unstoppable death.

Dr. Charles M. Herzfeld, director of the Pentagon's Advanced Research Projects Agency, had overseen the development of these new warheads. Not given to painting lurid pictures, Herzfeld nevertheless held them in awe. "It does not appear possible to build a missile defense system which a determined attacker can't get through," he said, indicating that this applied to both countries. In a reference to Soviet anti-ICBM claims, he added: "Perhaps the most serious danger would come from an overestimation of the value of an enemy defense by the enemy's policy makers. This could perhaps lead them into more aggressive adventures of danger to all."

Despite all the drawbacks, and the apparent futility, antimissile missiles appear to have some future. One possibility, long under deliberation, is to emplace them around Minuteman squadrons. The idea would be to make it harder for Russians in a first strike to knock out the ICBM's. Some cost studies have indicated it would be cheaper to protect the Minutemen with Nike-X than to build more Minutemen to insure the survivability of America's retaliatory striking force.

Planners also have been eying the system since the emergence of Communist China as a budding nuclear power. Some favored setting up Nike-X batteries to protect major cities from a suicidal attack or blackmail attempt by any country with a few nuclear weapons and from the possible accidental launch of an ICBM.

More than 500 million dollars has been spent by the United States in investigating ways of stopping ICBM's in space or shortly after they get off the launch pad. The only concept that looks at all workable is called Bambi and would require thousands of satellites equipped to intercept and destroy Soviet warheads. This would entail development of enormously complicated, fantastically expensive equipment. "It is difficult to make reliable estimates of the cost of such a system," Herzfeld has said. "But upkeep alone would run into the tens of billions of dollars per year." Bambi has never gotten off the drawing board.

It is against aircraft that the missile has come into its own as a defensive weapon.

The United States, Russia, England, and France have developed several varieties, all tailored to specific missions. The primary one, in which the United States and Russia have invested most heavily, is in providing continental defense against an armada of bombers. Others guard against air attack on the battlefield and protect naval units or are designed for air-to-air combat.

The evolution of continental air defense missiles in the United States and Russia has been strikingly similar. The U.S. Army brought forth the Nike-Ajax in 1953, a solid-fueled missile, and replaced it with the higher performance 75-mile-range Nike-Hercules in 1959. Meantime, the Air Force produced the Bomarc, which has both solid fuel and ramjet engines and is capable of intercepting aircraft at a distance of about 400 miles. At peak strength, some 1,500 Herculeses and Bomarcs were deployed on launchers around the United States and Canada. All were tied into the North American Air Defense Command (NORAD), which also maintained on instant readiness a force of 800 supersonic jet fighter planes armed with Genie and Falcon missiles and an Air National Guard force of 400 jets. For warning of an air attack, NORAD had built SAGE (Semi-Automatic Ground Environment) and the Distant Early Warning line of listening radars across northern Canada at a cost of more than 15 billion dollars. In the early 1960's, the DEW line was made largely obsolete by the 3-billion-dollar Ballistic Missile Early Warning Systems (BMEWS), comprised of giant radars in Scotland; Thule, Greenland and Alaska. BMEWS was designed to give a minimum of 15 minutes' warning of a mass ICBM attack coming over the top of the world, permitting Strategic Air Command bombers time to get off the ground. It could also detect an airborne attacking force.

The Soviet Union constructed a similar, but hardly as elaborate, radar network for its missile-jet fighter air defense system. The radars are positioned all around the perimeter of the country and many have air defense missiles nearby.

Russia's standby antiaircraft missile, frequently paraded through Moscow, has been given the name Guideline by the North Atlantic Treaty Organization. There are two types of Guidelines, the SA-2 and SA-3. Both are solid-fueled. The SA-3 is the more advanced and can perform along the lines of the Hercules. The SA-2 was credited with shooting down high-flying American U-2 spy planes over Cuba following the 1962 nuclear crisis precipitated by the deployment there of Soviet intermediate-range missiles. Guidelines have been deployed in Vietnam, where they shot down several U.S. planes, Egypt, Iraq and a number of Iron Curtain countries.

In 1963, the Russians unveiled a 48-foot antiaircraft missile carrying a radar reflector in its nose. The solid-fueled rocket, looking somewhat like a Nike-Zeus, has a range estimated at more than 150 miles and appears designed primarily to combat American supersonic B-58 bombers and the new SR-71, a 2,000-m.p.h. reconnaissance aircraft which replaced the U-2 in 1965.

Worthy of note is a tank-carried antiaircraft missile powered by a ramjet. It is a battlefield weapon primarily, but could defend cities with its estimated striking range of 45 miles.

Development of missiles to protect U.S. Army and Navy units from low-flying jets has proven extremely difficult for the United States. The best Army weapon is the Hawk, with a range of about 25 miles. It is mobile on trucks but is also extremely expensive. NATO countries have it. The Army attempted a radical improvement in the Mauler, designed for a tracked vehicle, but ran into technical problems that later forced abandonment of the project. As a substitute, the Army built a ground launcher for the air-to-air Sidewinder and named the new version of the missile the Chapparal. It also developed the Redeye, a tube-launched antiaircraft missile designed for infantrymen. But the cost of the new missiles was so high it was considering in 1965 bringing back ack-ack guns.

Tartar and Terrier were developed by the Navy, beginning in the early 1950's, to protect the fleet. Both short-range missiles, though, proved disappointing. They were not very accurate. In 1963, after the Navy had converted entirely to missiles, it was revealed that an "improvement program" costing some 300 million dollars had been ordered to make the two missiles function properly in combat. A sister missile, the 75-mile Talos, also proved troublesome for sailors to fire. And a fourth "T" — the Typhon — being developed to combat missiles as well as high-speed aircraft, had to be dropped in 1964. The radar and other gear for Typhon had grown so bulky it couldn't fit aboard the ships that had been built for it. The Navy went back to the drawing board and began working on a new concept, the Advanced Surface Missile System, which eventually was to replace Tartar, Terrier and Talos.

Russia has relatively few naval units. Only one marine antiaircraft missile has been identified. It has a range of 18 miles and looks like a cut-down Guideline. At one time it bore the name Golem IV.

Luckily the United States has excelled in air-to-

air missiles for today's high-speed jet fighters. Deadly Sidewinders, named after a rattlesnake found in the southwest United States, long have been standard equipment on Navy and Air Force planes. Equipped with an infrared guidance system which homes in on a jet's hot exhaust, Sidewinders have downed several Soviet MIG's flown by Red Chinese pilots. Even more deadly is the Navy's Sparrow III and the Air Force's Falcon series. For the new F-111B fighter the Navy is going up another step with the Phoenix missile. Fighter aircraft thus equipped are the main line of air defense for Army, Marine and Navy units.

Over the years the U.S. military has spent hundreds of millions of dollars on ECM — electronic countermeasures — to combat enemy air-launched missiles, such as Russia's M-100A, which is similar to Sidewinder. ECM include chaff made of foil and a variety of jamming devices to confuse or throw off course infrared and radar homing missiles. The big problem in employing ECM is knowing when a missile is headed at your aircraft.

Noteworthy among European air defense missiles are Britain's land-based Bloodhound and Thunderbird, both highly effective, and the shipboard Seacat and Seaslug. The Royal Air Force is equipped with high performance Red Top and Firestreak air-to-air missiles. France is relying on NATO Hawk and Nike-Hercules on the ground. But it is building the Masurca for Navy ships and MATRA 511 and 530 air-to-air missiles for its interceptors. Sweden and Italy also are in the air-to-air missile field. The missile armament for the United States-developed NATO fighter, the F-104, is the Sidewinder.

In sum, the cost of air and space defense systems, including airplanes, ships, missiles and electronic warning networks, has been staggering. The figure for the United States since the end of World War II easily surpasses 100 billion dollars. Soviet investment is high, too. One of the U.S. Air Force arguments for building an advanced manned bomber able to fly more than 2,000 miles per hour was that it would force the Russians to spend about 5 billion dollars to update their air defenses.

AIR-SPACE DEFENSE MISSILES

BOMARC B (U.S.)

Type: Surface-to-air (air breather).
Military service and designation: Air Force (CIM-10B).
Status: Operational.

Bomarc B rears from launcher.
—Boeing Co. photograph

Nike-Hercules on Formosa.
—U.S. Army photograph

Deployment: Location — continental United States (Duluth, Minn., Municipal Airport; Niagara Falls, N.Y., Municipal Airport; Kincheloe AFB, Kinross, Mich.; Langley AFB, Hampton, Va.; McGuire AFB, Wrightstown, N.J.; Otis AFB, Falmouth, Mass.) and Canada (North Bay, Ont., and La Macaza, Que.). Total authorized squadrons — 8 (6 in U.S., 2 in Canada). Squadron strength — 28 missiles.

Performance: Range — 400 nautical miles. Speed — supersonic. Ceiling — more than 70,000 ft.

Specifications: Length — 45 ft. Diameter — 35 in. Wingspan — 18 ft. Launch weight — 16,000 lbs. Guidance — command and radar homing. Warhead — nuclear or HE. Propulsion — solid and ramjet (2 RJ-43 advanced models). Stages — 2.

Principal contractors: Prime — Boeing. Frame — Boeing. Guidance—IBM, Westinghouse. Propulsion—Thiokol (solid booster); Marquardt (ramjet sustainer). Launcher — FMC.

History: R&D on the advanced Bomarc — the B model — began in 1958. Originally, a much larger number of squadrons was planned, but the decline in the bomber threat and pressure for budgetary cuts reduced the total squadrons to six in the United States. Bomarc B became initially operational in 1961. In March 1961, a Bomarc B launched from Eglin AFB, Fla., intercepted a simulated supersonic target 100,000 ft. over the Gulf of Mexico at a range of 446 statute miles.

NIKE-HERCULES (U.S.)

Type: Surface-to-air (antiaircraft and antimissile).

Military service and designation: Army (MIM-14A).

Status: Operational.

Deployment: Location — continental United States, Western Europe, the Far East. Total United States battalions — about 24. Battalion strength — 4 batteries. Battery strength — 9 launchers. Total launchers operational in United States — about 864.

Performance: Range — more than 75 nautical miles. Speed — Mach 3 plus. Ceiling — more than 150,000 ft.

Specifications: Length — 39 ft. Diameter — 31.5 in. Wingspan — 90 in. Launch weight — 10,000 lbs. Guidance — radio command. Warhead — nuclear or HE. Propulsion — solid. Stages — 2.

Principal contractors: Prime — Western Electric. Frame — Douglas. Guidance — Western Electric. Propulsion — Hercules (first stage); Thiokol (second stage). Launchers — Consolidated Western Steel.

History: Nike-Hercules is the second generation in the Nike missile family. R&D began in 1953. The missile became initially operational in 1958. New radars give the missile the capability of intercepting tactical missiles as well as very-high-performance jets. Mobile batteries make it possible to deploy Nike-Hercules in the field.

CANVAS COVERED MISSILE IN HOLD REVETMEN

NET COVERED LAUNCHERS

BULLDOZER BURYING TANK IN REVETMENT WALL

EHICLE REPAIR RAMP

CANVAS COVERED FRUIT SET SURROUNDED BY VERTICAL NETTING

CANVAS COVERED MISSILE TRAILERS

Guideline site in Cuba with six net-covered launchers, 1962. —U.S. Air Force photograph

GUIDELINE* (U.S.S.R.)

Type: Surface-to-air.

Military service and designation: Red Army (SA-2, SA-3).

Status: Operational.

Deployment: Location — with Soviet air defense forces, Army combat units, Iron Curtain nations, Egypt, Iraq, Cuba, North Vietnam.

Performance: Range — 20-25 miles. Altitude — 60,000 to 80,000 ft. Speed — 2,000-plus m.p.h.

Specifications: SA-2: Length — 23 ft. Diameter — 1.5 ft. Span — 6 ft. Weight — 2,700 lbs. Stages — 2. Guidance — radar beam rider. Propulsion — solid. SA-3: Length — 23 ft. Diameter — 2 ft. Span — 8 ft. Weight — 6,000 lbs. Stages — 2. Guidance — radar beam rider. Propulsion — solid. Warheads — HE.

History: Guidelines have been in the Soviet inventory since the mid-1950's. The improved version, SA-3, was introduced in 1962. The SA-2 is credited with shooting down American U-2's at over 60,000 ft. above Cuba.

* NATO designation.

LONG-RANGE AA MISSILE (U.S.S.R.)

Type: Surface-to-air.

Military Service: Red Army.

Status: Operational.

Deployment: Location — with air defense forces.

Performance: Range — about 150 miles. Altitude — 150,000 ft. Speed — 3,000-plus m.p.h.

Specifications: Length — 49 ft. Diameter — 2.5 ft. Span 13 ft. Weight — 20,000 lbs. Stages — 2. Guidance — radar homing. Propulsion — solid. Warhead — HE or nuclear.

History: Strikingly similar to the U.S. Nike-Zeus, this missile went into service in early 1964. It probably has some antimissile capability.

SHORT-RANGE AA MISSILE (U.S.S.R.)

Type: Surface-to-air.

Military service: Army and Navy.

Status: Operational.

Deployment: Location — with field units of the Red Army and aboard naval vessels.

Performance: Range — about 16 miles. Altitude — 50,000 ft. Speed — supersonic.

Specifications: Length — about 18 ft. Diameter — 1.5 ft. Weight — about 1,500 lbs. Stages — 2. Guidance — radio command. Propulsion — liquid with solid booster.

History: In service for several years, the missile is comparable to the U.S. Hawk. It is fired from a dual mounting, either on a truck chassis or rotatable launcher aboard ship.

Advanced SA-2 Guidelines, right, followed by long-range AA missiles, in Moscow.   —Tass photograph

Goa, 1965.
—Novosti Press Agency photograph

GOA* (U.S.S.R.)

Type: Surface-to-air (antiaircraft).

Military service: Army.

Status: Operational.

Deployment: Location— with division tank units.

Performance: Range — about 30 miles. Altitude — about 45,000 ft. Speed — supersonic.

Specifications: Length — about 25 ft. Diameter — 3.5 ft. Tailspan — 8 ft. Weight — about 4,000 lbs. Stages — 1. Guidance — radio command. Propulsion — liquid ramjet, with solid booster acceleration rockets (4).

History: Introduced in 1964, the missile is designed to protect mobile strike forces from supersonic jets swooping in close to the ground.

*NATO designation.

CT-41 (FRANCE)

Type: Surface-to-air (air breather).

Military service: Air Force.

Status: Experimental.

Deployment: None.

Performance: Range — 24.8 nautical miles. Speed — Mach 1.3. Ceiling — 130,000 ft.

Specifications: Length — 26.5 ft. Launch weight — 2,640 lbs. Guidance — radar homing. Stages — 2. Propulsion — solid booster and ramjet sustainer.

Principal contractor: Sud.

History: Latest in series of target drones (others: CT-10, CT-20) being used to develop tactical antiaircraft missiles.

PARCA (FRANCE)

Type: Surface-to-air.

Military service: Army.

Status: Operational.

Deployment: Location — mainly with antiaircraft training units.

Performance: Range — 10 miles. Speed — Mach 1.7. Ceiling — 80,000 ft.

Specifications: Length — 18 ft. Wingspan — 5.4 ft. Launch weight — 2,200 lbs. Guidance — radar command. Warhead — HE. Stages — 2. Propulsion — all solid.

Principal contractors: Prime — DEFA. Guidance — C. F. Thomson-Huston.

History: In service for several years, Parca is now undergoing advanced R&D to make it effective against Mach 3 aircraft.

Redeye.
—U. S. Army photograph

REDEYE (U.S.)

Type: Surface-to-air.

Military service and designation: Army and Marines (MIM-46A).

Status: Operational.

Deployment: Location — continental United States. Future — to be deployed with U.S. Army and Marine combat units in the United States and abroad.

Performance: Range — about 2 miles. Speed — supersonic. (Redeye is designed to intercept low-flying aircraft. One man can launch from shoulder.)

Specifications: Length — 4 ft. Diameter — 3 in. Launch weight — 20 lbs. Guidance — IR. Warhead — HE. Propulsion — solid. Stages — 1.

Principal contractors: Prime — Convair. Frame — Convair. Guidance — Philco, Convair. Propulsion — Atlantic Research.

History: Redeye was conceived to provide an infantryman with a weapon to combat jet aircraft over the battlefield. R&D began in 1958. The missile became initially operational in 1965. A Redeye is shipped and carried in and launched from the same disposable bazooka-shaped container.

Bloodhound.

BLOODHOUND I & II (GREAT BRITAIN)

Type: Surface-to-air.

Military service: Royal Air Force.

Status: Operational.

Deployment: Location — combat units in Britain and Australia; also purchased by Sweden and Switzerland.

Performance: Range — about 35 miles. Speed — Mach 2.5. Ceiling — treetop to high altitude.

Specifications: Length — 25.3 ft. Launch weight — 4,500 lbs. Guidance — radar homing. Warhead — HE. Propulsion — cluster of 4 solid boosters; liquid sustainer.

Principal contractors: Prime — Bristol Aircraft. Guidance — Ferranti. Propulsion — Bristol Siddeley.

History: R&D began about 1949. Bloodhound I became initially operational in 1958, Bloodhound II in 1961.

THUNDERBIRD (GREAT BRITAIN)

Type: Surface-to-air.

Military service: Army.

Status: Operational.

Deployment: Location — Army combat units.

Performance: Range — 25 nautical miles. Speed — about Mach 2.

Specifications: Length — about 19 ft. Wingspan — 5.6 in. Guidance — radar homing. Warhead — HE. Stages — 2. Propulsion — solid.

Principal contractors: Prime — English Electric. Guidance — Marconi. Propulsion — Bristol Siddeley, ICI.

History: R&D began in early 1950's; first operational in 1959. An advanced Thunderbird, launched from mobile carriers, is in production. It has a greater range and low-level capability.

Thunderbird.
—British Information Services
photograph

Hawk.

HAWK (U.S.)

Type: Surface-to-air.

Military service and designation: Army and Marines (MIM-23A).

Status: Operational.

Deployment: Location — continental United States. Battalions — 2 (Army), 1 (Marines). Battalion strength — 3 to 5 batteries. Battery strength — 6 to 12 launchers (3 missiles per launcher). Also deployed in Europe, Far East, and Panama.

Performance: Range — about 22 nautical miles. Speed — Mach 2 plus. Ceiling — treetop level to about 40,000 ft. (Hawk is specifically designed for use against low-flying aircraft but has intercepted such tactical missiles as the Honest John, Little John, and Corporal in tests.)

Specifications: Length — 17 ft. Diameter — 14 in. Wingspan — 4 ft. Launch weight — 1,275 lbs. Guidance — semiactive radar homing. Warhead — HE. Stages — 2. Propulsion — solid.

Principal contractors: Prime — Raytheon. Frame — Raytheon, Northrop. Guidance — Raytheon. Propulsion — Aerojet.

History: R&D began in 1953, production in 1957. Hawk was initially operational in 1959. It is being produced under license by NATO countries.

TIGERCAT (GREAT BRITAIN)

Type: Surface-to-air.

Military service: Army.

Status: R&D.

Deployment: None.

Performance: Similar to the Seacat, from which it evolves. To be launched from armored carriers.

Specifications: None available, but apparently close to Seacat.

Principal contractor: Prime — Short Bros.

History: R&D began in 1960.

R-422B3.

—MATRA photograph

R-422B3 (FRANCE)

Type: Surface-to-air.

Military service: Army.

Status: Operational since 1960.

Deployment: Location — with combat troops on mobile carriers.

Performance: Range — about 60 nautical miles. Speed — Mach 2.6.

Specifications: Length — 30.5 ft. Wingspan — about 6 ft. Finspan — about 9 ft. Launch weight — 3,500 lbs. Guidance — radar command/homing. Warhead — HE. Stages — 2. Propulsion — all solid.

Principal contractor: MATRA.

SEABORNE AIR-SPACE DEFENSE MISSILES

Talos.

—U.S. Navy photograph

TALOS (U.S.)

Type: Surface-to-air and surface-to-surface (air breather).

Military service and designation: Navy (RIM-8E).

Status: Operational.

Deployment: Location — aboard four cruisers, **U.S.S. Galveston, U.S.S. Little Rock, U.S.S. Oklahoma City,** and the nuclear-powered **U.S.S. Long Beach.** Future — authorized for three more cruisers, **U.S.S. Albany, U.S.S. Columbus,** and **U.S.S. Chicago.** The converted missile cruisers **Albany** and **Columbus** were commissioned in 1962, the **Chicago** in 1963.

Performance: Range — more than 65 nautical miles. Speed — about Mach 2.5. Ceiling — extremely high altitude.

Specifications: Length — about 30 ft. Diameter — about 30 in. Launch weight — 7,000 lbs. (booster alone weighs 4,000 lbs.). Guidance — radar. Warhead — nuclear or HE. Propulsion — solid (first stage), ramjet (second stage).

Principal contractors: Prime — Bendix. Frame — McDonnell. Guidance — Bendix, Sperry. Propulsion — Allegany. Automatic loading system — GE.

History: Talos is an outgrowth of the Bumblebee program initiated at Johns Hopkins University's Applied Physics Lab in 1945. R&D on Talos began in 1948. The missile became initially operational aboard the **Galveston** in 1959.

Terriers on land with the Marines.
—U.S. Marine Corps photograph

TERRIER (U.S.)

Type: Surface-to-air and surface-to-surface.

Military service and designation: Navy and Marines (RIM-2E).

Status: Operational.

Deployment: Location — aboard 15 ships (6 cruisers: **U.S.S. Boston, U.S.S. Canberra, U.S.S. Providence, U.S.S. Springfield, U.S.S. Topeka, U.S.S. Long Beach;** 3 carriers: **U.S.S. Kitty Hawk, U.S.S. Constitution,** nuclear-powered **U.S.S. Enterprise;** 1 destroyer: **U.S.S. Gyatt;** 10 frigates: **U.S.S. Farragut, U.S.S. Luce, U.S.S. Coontz, U.S.S. King, U.S.S. Mahan, U.S.S. Dewey, U.S.S. Preble, U.S.S. Dahlgren, U.S.S. MacDonough, U.S.S. W. V. Pratt**). A

Terriers at sea.
—General Dynamics Corp. photograph

mobile version used with Marine units. Future — authorized for 17 more guided-missile frigates.

Performance: Range — 10 nautical miles. Speed — supersonic. Ceiling — more than 50,000 ft. (Advanced Terrier has about a 100% improvement in performance.)

Specifications: Length — 27 ft. Diameter — 12 in. Launch weight — about 3,000 lbs. Guidance — radar. Warhead — HE. Propulsion — solid. Stages — 2.

Principal contractors: Prime — Convair. Frame — Convair. Guidance — Reeves, FTL, and Sperry. Propulsion — Allegany.

History: Terrier is an outgrowth of the Bumblebee program (see Talos). R&D began in 1949. The first Terriers were initially operational in 1956. Advanced Terriers were first deployed in 1960 aboard the frigate **Dewey.**

Tartar.
—U.S. Navy photograph

TARTAR (U.S.)

Type: Surface-to-air.

Military service and designation: Navy (RIM-24B).

Status: Operational.

Deployment: Location — aboard 9 destroyers, **U.S.S. C. F. Adams, U.S.S. John King, U.S.S. Wilson, U.S.S. McCormack, U.S.S. Towers, U.S.S. Sampson, U.S.S. Lawrence, U.S.S. Sellers, U.S.S. Robison.** Future — authorized for 14 more destroyers. Four — **U.S.S. Biddle, U.S.S. Barney, U.S.S. Hoel,** and **U.S.S. Buchanan** — were commissioned in 1962.

Performance: Range — more than 10 nautical miles. Speed — supersonic. Ceiling — high altitude.

Specifications: Length — 15 ft. Diameter — 12 in. Launch weight — about 1,500 lbs. Guidance — beam rider. Warhead — HE. Propulsion — solid. Stages — 2.

Principal contractors: Prime — Convair. Frame — Convair. Guidance — Raytheon. Propulsion — Aerojet.

History: One of the Bumblebee missile family. R&D on Tartar began in 1955. The missile became initially operational aboard the **U.S.S. C. F. Adams** in 1961.

GOLEM III (U.S.S.R.)

Type: Underwater-to-air and surface-to-air.

Military service: Navy.

Status: Operational.

Deployment: Location — installations on surface vessels and possibly some submarines.

Performance: Range — 10 miles. Ceiling — not available. Speed — probably about Mach 2.

Specifications: Length — 15 to 20 ft. Diameter — 20 in. Guidance — IR. Warhead — HE. Stages — 2. Propulsion — all solid.

GOLEM IV (U.S.S.R.)

Type: Surface-to-air.

Military service: Navy.

Status: Operational.

Deployment: Location — aboard surface vessels.

Performance: Range — reported to be 45 miles. Ceiling — not available. Speed — Mach 2.5.

Specifications: Length — not available. Guidance — radar. Warhead — HE. Propulsion — solid.

MASALCA (FRANCE)

Type: Surface-to-air (air breather).

Military service: Navy.

Status: Operational.

Deployment: Location — aboard French cruisers.

Performance: Range — about 65 nautical miles. Ceiling — secret.

Specifications: Launch weight — about 6,000 lbs. Guidance — beam rider. Warhead — HE. Stages — 2. Propulsion — solid booster, liquid-fueled ramjet sustainer.

Principal contractor: SIAL.

MASURCA (FRANCE)

Type: Surface-to-air.

Military service: Navy.

Status: Operational since 1960.

Deployment: Location — installations going aboard new pocket cruisers, escort vessels, and helicopter carrier **Jeanne d'Arc.**

Performance: Range — 25 nautical miles. Speed — Mach 1.9. Ceiling — high altitude.

Specifications: Length — 18.5 ft. Wingspan — 3 ft. Launch weight — 3,200 lbs. Guidance — radar beam rider. Warhead — HE. Stages — 2. Propulsion — all solid.

Principal contractor: Ruelle Arsenal.

History: Masurca was conceived as the mainstay of the French Navy's air defense. There are two advanced models now under development.

Seacat.

SEACAT (GREAT BRITAIN)

Type: Ship-to-air.

Military service: Royal Navy.

Status: Operational.

Deployment: Location — aboard destroyers and cruisers. It is being installed in units of the West German, New Zealand, Australian, and Swedish navies.

Performance: Range — about 4 miles. Speed — Mach 1.

Specifications: Length — 4 ft. 10 in. Wingspan — 2 ft.

Guidance — radio command. Warhead — HE. Stages — 2. Propulsion — solid.

Principal contractor: Prime — Short Bros.

History: R&D began in mid-1950's. Seacat first became operational in 1960. There are four missiles to a battery.

Seaslug.
—Sir W. G. Armstrong Whitworth Aircraft, Ltd. photograph

SEASLUG (GREAT BRITAIN)

Type: Surface-to-air.

Military service: Royal Navy.

Status: Operational.

Deployment: Location — aboard guided-missile destroyers.

Performance: Range — about 15 miles. Speed — Mach 3.

Specifications: Length — 19.5 ft. Diameter — 1.5 ft. Wingspan — 4.5 ft. Guidance — radio beam rider. Warhead — HE. Stages — 2. Propulsion — solid.

Principal contractors: Prime — W. G. Armstrong. Guidance — GE.

History: R&D began in about 1956. Operational in 1961. Seaslug is fired in batteries.

ANTIMISSILE MISSILES

NIKE-X/ZEUS (U.S.)

Type: Surface-to-air antisatellite.

Military service: Army.

Status: Late R&D.

Deployment: Location — on Kwajalein atoll as potential antisatellite weapon.

Performance: Range — about 100 nautical miles. Speed — about Mach 4.

Nike-Zeus.
—U. S. Army photograph

Specifications: Length — 43 ft. Diameter — 5 ft. Guidance — radio command. Warhead — nuclear. Propulsion — solid. Stages — 3. Thrust of first stage — 450,000 lbs.

Principal contractors: Prime — Western Electric. Frame — Douglas. Guidance — Western Electric. Propulsion — Thiokol. Launcher — Douglas.

History: R&D on Zeus began in 1957. Starting in 1960, the Army made several bids to deploy the system but was turned down because of the more than 8-billion-dollar cost to protect most of the country. Tests in 1963-1964 against new United States warheads showed Zeus ineffective against decoys. The program was reoriented around a better radar — the X concept — and changed to an experimental intercepter of low-flying satellites. See Nike-X/Sprint.

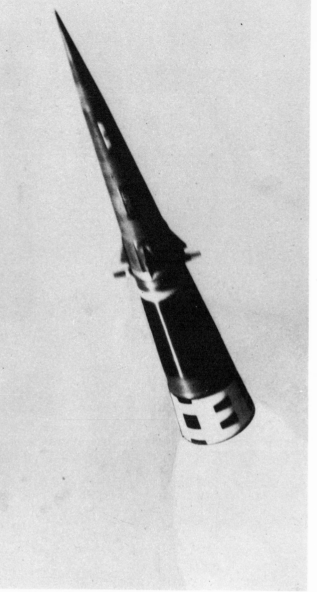

Nike-X/Sprint.

NIKE-X/SPRINT (U.S.)

Type: Surface-to-air anti-ICBM.

Military service: Army.

Status: R&D.

Deployment: None.

Performance: Range — 30 miles (overhead). Speed — 10,000-plus m.p.h.

Specifications: Length — 27 ft. Diameter at base — about 5 ft. Weight — not disclosed. Stages — 2. Guidance — radar command. Propulsion — high energy solid.

Principal contractors: Prime — Western Electric. Guidance — BTL. Propulsion — Hercules. Pop-up launcher — Martin.

History: Development started in 1963 as a means of stopping ICBM warheads after they have entered the atmosphere over their targets. Tests of the Sprint, which has highest acceleration of any

United States missile, began in 1965. It is popped from an underground cell by an explosive charge, like Polaris, and ignited in the air. Cost of deploying the system to protect most of the United States was estimated at upwards of 20 billion dollars plus fallout shelters. Cheaper "point defense" for ICBM sites and major cities was under consideration. ARPA was conducting a corollary R&D program with Boeing on the booster to check an alternate high-acceleration propellant, Hibex.

Large container frequently paraded by Soviets, some Western observers believe, contains a solid-fueled anti-ICBM. Movies released by the Russians indicate the missile may be fired through the cap, right, from a silo emplacement.

ANTI-ICBM (U.S.S.R.)

Claims of an antimissile missile which could "knock a fly out of the sky" were made in 1962 by then Premier Nikita Khrushchev. But the Russians never displayed such a weapon publicly and it was believed they were having as difficult a time as the United States in perfecting a system able to combat decoys and maneuverable warheads. See Long-Range AA Missile (U.S.S.R.).

AIR-TO-AIR MISSILES

GENIE (U.S.)

Type: Air-to-air.

Military service and designation: Air Force (AIR-2A).

Deployment: Location — carried in continental United States and overseas by aircraft of the Air Defense Command, Tactical Air Command, and European and Pacific Commands (F-89, F-101, F-106).

Performance: Range — about 6 nautical miles. Speed — supersonic.

Specifications: Length — 9.5 ft. Diameter — 1.3 ft. Launch weight — about 800 lbs. Guidance — free flight. Warhead — nuclear. Propulsion — solid.

Principal contractors: Prime — Douglas. Frame — Douglas. Propulsion — Aerojet.

History: Genie was the first United States air-to-air missile carrying a nuclear warhead. Development of the missile began in 1955. Genie was initially operational in 1958.

The Falcon family.
—Hughes Aircraft Co. photograph

FALCON (U.S.)

Type: Air-to-air.

Military service and designation: Air Force (AIM-4A, 4E, 47A, 26B [nuclear]).

Status: Operational.

Deployment: Location — continental United States and overseas on aircraft of Air Defense Command, Tactical Air Command, and European and Pacific Commands (F-89, F-101, F-102, and F-106).

Performance: Range — about 5 nautical miles (AIM-4A, 4E), greater for advanced models. Speed — supersonic.

Specifications: Length — 6.5 to 7 ft. (AIM-4A and 4E), 7 ft. 11 in. (AIM-26B). Wingspan — 20 in. Launch weight — more than 120 lbs. (AIM-4A and 4E), more than 200 lbs. (AIM-26B). Guidance — radar homing, IR. Warhead — HE and nuclear. Propulsion — solid. Stages — 1.

Principal contractors: Prime — Hughes. Frame — Hughes. Guidance — Hughes. Propulsion — Thiokol.

History: Development of the Falcon began in 1949. It became initially operational in 1957. Planes carry mixed loads of Falcons with IR and radar guidance. The nuclear Super Falcon, successor to the Genie, became initially operational in 1961.

SPARROW III (U.S.)

Type: Air-to-air.

Military service and designation: Navy (AIM-7E).

Sparrow III's aboard a Navy F3H-2 Demon.
—U.S. Navy photograph

Status: Operational.

Deployment: Location — carrier-based U.S. Navy aircraft. Also with Marine units.

Performance: Range — more than 5 nautical miles. Speed — more than Mach 3.

Specifications: Length — 12 ft. Diameter — 8 in. Launch weight — 400 lbs. Guidance — radar homing. Warhead — HE. Stages — 1. Propulsion — solid. (A new version under development has a packaged liquid propellant.) Thrust (solid) — 7,800 lbs.

Principal contractors: Prime — Raytheon. Frame — Raytheon. Guidance — Raytheon. Propulsion — Aerojet. (Thiokol working on new version.)

History: Sparrow I development began in 1951; production of Sparrow III began in 1957. Sparrow III became initially operational in 1958. It gave the Navy an all-weather air-to-air missile, when Sidewinder had only IR guidance, which is inhibited by clouds.

SIDEWINDER (U.S.)

Type: Air-to-air.

Military service and designation: Navy (AIM-9B) and Air Force (AIM-9D).

Status: Operational.

Deployment: Location — carrier-based Navy aircraft and aircraft of Air Defense Command. Also widely used by United States allies in Europe and Far East.

Performance: Range — about 2 nautical miles. Speed — supersonic. Ceiling — more than 50,000 ft.

Specifications: Length — 9 ft. Diameter — 5 in. Launch weight — about 155 lbs. Guidance — IR or radar homing. (New 1C version has switchable guidance package.) Warhead — HE. Stages — 1. Propulsion — solid.

Sidewinder.
—U.S. Navy photograph

Principal contractors: Prime — Philco, GE. Frame — Norris Thermador, Hunter Douglas. Guidance — Philco, GE. Propulsion — NAA.

History: NOTS at China Lake, Calif., began R&D about 1950. Sidewinder was initially operational in 1956. Nationalist Chinese aircraft successfully used Sidewinders against the Red Chinese over Formosa Strait in 1958. Army version is called Chaparral.

M-100 A (U.S.S.R.)

Type: Air-to-air.

Military service: Air Force.

Status: Operational.

Deployment: Location — reported seen on Soviet fighter planes, but apparently never included in MIG jet equipment given the Red Chinese.

Performance: Range — 3.5 miles. Speed — Mach 2.5.

Specifications: Length — about 10 ft. Guidance — semi-active radio/radar command. Warhead — HE. Propulsion — solid.

PHOENIX (U.S.)

Type: Air-to-air.

Military service and designation: Navy (AIM-54A).

Status: R&D.

Deployment: Intended for the F-111B (TFX).

Performance: Not disclosed.

Specifications: Propulsion — solid. Other details not disclosed.

Principal contractors: Prime — Hughes. Propulsion — Rocketdyne.

History: Development began in 1964. The weapon, an outgrowth of the Falcon family will be the major armament of the Navy's new F-111B.

Firestreaks being fitted to an RAF Javelin.
—de Havilland Aircraft Co., Ltd. photograph

FIRESTREAK (GREAT BRITAIN)

Type: Air-to-air.

Military service: Royal Air Force and Royal Navy.

Status: Operational.

Deployment: Location — carried by interceptors of RAF and air units of the Royal Navy.

Performance: Range — about 5 nautical miles. Speed — Mach 2.3.

Specifications: Length — 10.5 ft. Diameter — 8.5 in. Launch weight — 300 lbs. Guidance — IR. Warhead — HE. Propulsion — solid. Stages — 1.

Principal contractor: Prime — de Havilland.

AS 20 (FRANCE)

Type: Air-to-air and air-to-surface.

Military service: Air Force and Navy.

Status: Operational.

Deployment: Location — carried by Air Force and Navy aircraft in Europe, Africa and the Mediterranean.

Performance: Range — 2.5 miles. Speed — supersonic.

Specifications: Length — 8.5 ft. Launch weight — 295 lbs. (air-to-air model), about 340 lbs. (air-to-surface model). Guidance — radio command. Warhead — HE. Propulsion — solid. Stages — 2.

Principal contractor: Prime — Nord.

History: AS 20 has been adopted by NATO forces. Its NATO designation is AA5103.

R-511 (FRANCE)

Type: Air-to-air.

Military service: Air Force.

Status: Operational.

Deployment: Location — carried by French Air Force jet interceptors.

Performance: Range — about 5 miles. Speed — supersonic.

Specifications: Length — 10 ft. Diameter — 10 in. Launch weight — about 400 lbs. Guidance — semipassive electromagnetic. Warhead — HE. Propulsion — solid. Stages — 2. Thrust — 3,500 lbs. (first); 440 lbs. (second).

Principal contractors: Prime — MATRA. Propulsion — Hotchkiss-Brandt.

History: The R-511 is to be replaced by the advanced MATRA R-530.

C-7 (ITALY)

Type: Air-to-air.

Military service: Air Force.

Status: Operational.

Deployment: Location — interceptors of the Italian Air Force.

Performance: Range — 6 miles. Speed — Mach 1.9.

Specifications: Length — 6.5 ft. Wingspan — 25 in. Diameter — 6 in. Launch weight — 155 lbs. Guidance — IR or radar. Warhead — HE (55 lbs.). Propulsion — solid.

Principal contractors: Prime — SISPRE. Propulsion — Thiokol, Bombrini.

FRIDA (SWEDEN)

Type: Air-to-air.

Military service: Air Force.

Status: Operational.

Deployment: Location — carried by Saab, Lansen, and Draken interceptors.

Performance: Range — about 5 miles. Speed — supersonic.

Specifications: Length — about 6 ft. Diameter — about 5 in. Launch weight — about 90 lbs. Warhead — HE (39 lbs.).

Principal contractors: Prime — Bofors. Fire control — Saab.

History: An improved version, Gerda, also is being produced.

RED TOP (GREAT BRITAIN)

Type: Air-to-air.

Military service: Royal Air Force.

Status: R&D.

Deployment: Location — to replace Firestreaks on various aircraft.

Performance: Range — about 9.5 nautical miles. Speed — about Mach 3.

Specifications: Length — 10.6 ft. Wingspan — 3 ft. Diameter — 8.75 in. Guidance — IR. Warhead — HE (68 lbs.). Propulsion — solid. Stages — 1.

Principal contractor: Prime — de Havilland.

Red Top.

R-530 (FRANCE)

Type: Air-to-air.

Military service: Air Force and Navy.

Status: Late R&D.

Deployment: Location — to be carried by Mirage III and Sud Vautour jet interceptors.

Performance: Range — 10 miles. Speed — Mach 1.1.

Specifications: Length — about 6.5 ft. Guidance — IR or electromagnetic. Warhead — HE. Propulsion — solid. Stages — 2.

Principal contractors: Prime — MATRA. Propulsion — Hotchkiss-Brandt.

TAAM-1D (JAPAN)

Type: Air-to-air.

Military service: Air Force.

Status: R&D.

Deployment: Location — to be carried by Japanese interceptors.

Performance: Range — about 1.5 miles. Speed — Mach 1.5.

Specifications: Length — 8 ft. Launch weight — 335 lbs. Guidance — IR. Warhead — HE.

Principal contractor: Prime — Fuji.

TMA-1 (JAPAN)

Type: Air-to-air.

Military service: Air Force.

Status: R&D.

Deployment: Location — to be carried by Japanese interceptors.

Performance: Speed — supersonic.

Specifications: Length — about 10 ft. Launch weight — more than 200 lbs. Warhead — HE. Propulsion — solid.

Principal contractors: Prime — Mitsubishi, Mitsubishi Electric. Propulsion — Fuji.

Dr. Robert H. Goddard, U.S. rocket pioneer, and the world's first successful liquid-fueled rocket at Auburn, Mass., in 1926.

—NASA photograph

7

THE LONG WAY UP

The great missiles and spacecraft of today are at the center of the technological explosion of the twentieth century.

The huge, flaming mechanical beasts and the shimmering spacecraft feed and fatten without cease on dozens of expanding scientific and technical fields. In less than 25 years the rocket has grown from a scientific plaything to a nuclear-tipped weapon capable of spanning oceans and continents. In less than ten years it has grown into vehicles capable of hurling men into space and to the moon and scientific instruments to nearby planets.

Still the drumming pace quickens. But, in the beginning, it was slow enough.

The rocket enters recorded history on the plains of China.

The occasion was the besieging of the city of Kai-fung-fu by units of the Mongol horde. The date was A.D. 1232 — five years after the death of Genghis Khan.

According to a Chinese chronicle, the Chinese defenders of Kai-fung-fu sought to destroy or at least discourage the Mongols by launching mysterious "arrows of fire" at them. Further description indicates that these "arrows" were self-propelled rockets powered by burning black powder.

The art of making rockets — or Chinese arrows as they were often called in the Middle Ages — spread throughout Eurasia over the next century. Word moved westward over the trade routes. Long

before the century was out, the Arabs published technical instructions on rocket making. And by the early 1300's the rocket had been introduced into Europe.

But no one was greatly impressed.

Various types of rockets, all of them quite small, were used for a hundred years or more in both land and sea warfare. They were particularly effective in igniting the tarred rigging of sailing ships. They also were used as incendiaries in land sieges. However, by the mid-sixteenth century the war rocket fell into disuse. The rocket was assigned only the more humble tasks of providing signals and fireworks displays.

Nowhere was the rocket more beloved for its use in fireworks displays than in Czarist Russia. Peter the Great in the early 1700's established a special rocket works in St. Petersburg and personally supervised the manufacture of great quantities of skyrockets for numerous royal celebrations.

However, not until almost another 100 years had passed did the war rocket undergo a brief renaissance, thanks to the Indian Prince of Mysore.

The Indians at this time had taken the type of rocket that the British used for fireworks and converted it into a formidable weapon. Instead of a cardboard tube, the Indians substituted iron. Instead of weighing only a few pounds, the Indian rocket weighed six to twelve. These large iron rockets were fitted to long bamboo poles to stabilize and guide them in flight. They had a range of more than a mile.

The Prince of Mysore established a corps of rocket gunners. It numbered about 5,000. The result was that the British Army in India suffered a number of serious maulings, and British Army officials in England began to look again at the potentialities of the war rocket.

Colonel — later Sir — William Congreve provided the British authorities with what they were looking for. He began by experimenting with the biggest skyrockets available and developed a 40-inch-long incendiary war rocket in 1805. The following year thousands of Congreve rockets launched from British ships burned much of the French port of Boulogne, and the next year the British gutted Copenhagen the same way.

The fame of the Congreve rocket swept much of the world. Armies from Russia to America established rocket units. And Congreve designed a variety of war rockets. Some weighed up to nearly 50 pounds and had a range of 3,000 yards. When he died, Congreve had been planning rockets that weighed more than 500 pounds.

However, the rocket was eclipsed by great improvements in artillery ballistics, making the conventional cannon a far more effective weapon. Once more the rocket was consigned to being used for signals and entertainment. For another century rocketry was in the hands of dreamers and scientific prophets ranging in seriousness from the French novelist Jules Verne to the Russian inventor Konstantin Tsiolkovsky.

Then, between World War I and World War II, came a great seeding time. Rocketry was generally considered a technical curiosity. It was greatly overshadowed by the very great and dramatic advances in aeronautics. But in this period the first major advances beyond the 800-year-old black-powder rocket were made. The theme was set by two scientific papers.

The first was written in 1919 by Dr. Robert Hutchens Goddard, a professor at Clark University in Worcester, Massachusetts. The paper was called "A Method of Reaching Extreme Altitudes." It explored the possibility of using rockets to carry scientific instruments into the outer reaches of the earth's atmosphere. It also discussed the possibility of sending a rocket to the moon.

The second paper was written by Herman Oberth in 1923. He called it "The Rocket into Interplanetary Space." It sought to demonstrate that rockets could be designed that would be capable of placing satellites in orbit and operating in interplanetary space.

Goddard designed and built a rocket engine fueled with gasoline and liquid oxygen. On March 16, 1926, he successfully launched a small rocket propelled by his new engine at Auburn, Massachusetts. It traveled to an altitude of 184 feet at a speed of 60 miles per hour. Primitive as this experiment was, it opened the way to the stars.

Goddard's work was ignored as so much scientific tinkering by his countrymen. Germany — and then Russia — took rockets far more seriously. Within a decade of Goddard's first rocket flight, both countries had mounted rather impressive rocket programs. Not so America. It tarried until 1942 to organize its rocket researchers.

Following in the technical path opened by Oberth, German scientists and engineers in the 1920's and 1930's began the work that led to the development of the first great war rockets of the twentieth century — the V-1 and the far more deadly V-2.

As early as 1928, a German test pilot flew a rocket-powered glider for about one mile. Johannes Winkler launched the first European liquid-fueled rocket in 1931. And in 1932 the German Army formally began a rocket-development program under Dr. Walter Dornberger, then a captain but later to be a general in charge of the famed German rocket test center at Peenemünde on the Baltic coast. Among the bright young men who joined the new Army rocket program was Dr. Wernher von Braun.

The V-1, which the Germans developed first at Peenemünde, was a jet-powered pilotless aircraft. But the V-2 liquid-fueled ballistic missile was something revolutionary. It was nearly 47 feet tall and 5 feet, 5 inches in diameter. Fully fueled with liquid oxygen and alcohol, it weighed 14 tons. It flew at 3,300 miles an hour, soared 60 miles above the earth, and struck targets 190 miles away with a high-explosive warhead about the size of a 2,000-pound bomb. Nothing could stop it once it was launched.

Hitler's secret rockets were ready on September 6, 1944. The first two were fired at Paris. One fell short; the other crashed into the city. Two days later, just before seven o'clock in the evening, a V-2 thundered into Chiswick, England. Three persons were killed, ten injured. A few seconds later a second V-2 struck some wooden huts near Epping. A new era in warfare had begun.

During the next seven months, the retreating German Army launched more than 1,300 V-2's at England. The mobile V-2's were hidden in the countryside by day, then swiftly moved to ever-new launching sites at night. Meantime, Dornberger, von Braun, and the other rocket wizards at Peenemünde were preparing fresh surprises. They were designing far larger missiles, which would have been capable of striking America.

But they were too late. Nazi Germany was doomed. The Allied armies swept in from the west and the east. The last V-2 launched in the war pounded Antwerp in March. The rocket scientists and engineers fled southward, leaving a wrecked Peenemünde to be captured by the Russians.

The Russians and Americans divided the rocket spoils. Both sides seized large quantities of V-2 parts and documents. The U.S. Army recruited many of the Peenemünde group, including Dornberger and von Braun, to work in the United States. At the same time, the Russians shanghaied hundreds of German scientists and engineers to work in camps in the Soviet Union.

Of the two great powers, only Russia was very seriously interested. The Soviets sought to begin a rocket-development program from the point where the Germans had stopped. On the other hand, the United States disregarded the Soviet menace and sought only to disarm. As a result, the Soviets moved ahead rapidly in the development of missiles over the next five to eight years. Efforts in the United States were fitful at best. The only major programs were in the field of such air-breathing missiles as the Regulus and the abortive Navaho — essentially, pilotless jet aircraft.

One of the principal reasons why the United States did not press ahead with the development of the ICBM in the late 1940's was the great weight of the atomic-bomb warheads in that period. A missile capable of hurling the 10,000-pound warheads of that time would have had to be almost three times as large as the Atlas which the United States later developed. However, this obstacle did not dismay the Soviets. By beginning work on a missile of such magnitude, they stole an early lead, not only in building ICBM's, but in space exploration as well.

From the end of World War II to mid-1954 the United States spent only about 6.5 million dollars on long-range ballistic missiles. That would be the cost of only four Polarises in 1966. Then in 1954 the trend was reversed.

United States intelligence reports offered increasing evidence that Russia was well on the way toward the development of ballistic missiles of both intermediate and intercontinental range. Also, U.S. scientists had not only designed the far more powerful hydrogen bomb, but also had found ways to reduce it to much more manageable size.

Between 1954 and the last half of the 1960's, the United States developed whole families of ballistic missiles from short-range antitank and air-to-air missiles to the gigantic 7.5-million-pound-thrust Saturn V's for the Apollo moon program. The rapidity of the developmental pace has been dizzying.

No sooner were the Atlas and Titan proclaimed the wonders of the Space Age than they were declared obsolete. Dozens of missile and space projects in varying states of development have been bypassed by technology and junked. Never before has it been possible to fill a museum with technological relics and curiosities in so short a time.

The cost has been as impressive as the size of the latest rockets.

The budget of the National Aeronautics and Space Administration alone had reached more than 5 billion dollars by the mid-1960's. That amounted to 25 per cent of all the money spent in the United States by government and industry on research and development.

Conservative officials have estimated that the total cost of the Apollo program will reach about 20 billion dollars by 1970. More pessimistic officials have forecast a total cost of nearly 40 billion dollars.

This is the central thrust that is behind much of the scientific and technological revolution of the second half of the twentieth century.

BEGINNINGS

CONGREVE ROCKET (GREAT BRITAIN)

Type: Surface-to-surface (mobile).

Military service: Navy and Army.

Status at time dropped: Operational.

Deployment: Location — Congreve rockets were used by both Army and Navy units. They also were used widely in Europe, as were copies and variations of the original models.

Performance: Range — about 3,000 yards.

Specifications: Length — 40.5 in. (plus 16-ft. guiding stick). Diameter — 3.5 in. Launch weight — 32 lbs. Guidance — free flight. Warhead — incendiary. Propulsion — solid (black powder).

History: R&D began about 1801. Sir William Congreve developed his rockets from skyrockets then used for fireworks demonstrations. The initial success operationally came in 1806 when Congreve rockets launched from ships devastated Boulogne. The following year thousands of ship-launched Congreve rockets burned out much of Copenhagen. Later models of Congreve rockets varied from about 10 to 42 pounds.

V-1 (GERMANY)

Type: Surface-to-surface (air breather).

Military service and designation: Air Force (Fi 103).

Status at time dropped: Operational.

Deployment: Location — Nazi-occupied Europe.

Performance: Range — 150 miles. Speed — 360 m.p.h.

Specifications: Length — 25.4 ft. Wingspan — 17.67 ft. Guidance — autopilot. Warhead — HE (2,200 lbs.). Propulsion — pulse-jet.

History: R&D began about 1942 by the **Luftwaffe** at Peenemünde. A V-1 was launched successfully across the English Channel to England June 13, 1944, for the first time. More than 8,000 V-1's were launched against England. Casualties totalled more than 45,000. The V-1 "blitz" was ended by the destruction and capture of the launching ramps on the Channel coast.

Captured German V-2 prepared for launching at White Sands Missile Range, N. M., in 1946.

—U.S. Army photograph

A V-2 carrying a WAC Corporal second stage on February 24, 1949, reached a record altitude of 250 miles.

—U.S. Army photograph

V-2 (GERMANY)

Type: Surface-to-surface (mobile).

Military service: Army.

Status at time dropped: Operational.

Deployment: Location — units of the Nazi German Army in Western Europe.

Performance: Range — 190 miles. Speed — about 3,600 m.p.h. Apogee — 60 miles.

Specifications: Length — 46 ft. 11 in. Diameter — 5 ft. 5 in. Launch weight — 28,229 lbs. Guidance — radio command. Warhead — HE (2,200 lbs.). Propulsion — liquid (LOX and ethyl alcohol). Stages — 1. Thrust — 59,500 lbs.

History: R&D began on the world's first long-range ballistic missile about 1936. The V-2, or A-4, was developed by the German rocket center at Peenemünde on the Baltic Coast. The first V-2 was launched June 13, 1942. The first completely successful flight took place that same year on October 3. The V-2 test missile flew 118 miles. The first operational launching took place September 6, 1944, when two V-2's were launched against Paris and one fell short. On September 8, 1944, at 6:43 P.M., a V-2 fired from the Netherlands struck London for the first time. More than 1,300 operational V-2's were launched against England before the end of World War II. Total casualties: some 9,000 dead and wounded. The V-2 originally was designed to be fired from fixed bunkers; later, when the first bunkers were destroyed in bombing raids, the V-2 was moved from place to place on special trucks — the **Vidalwagen** and **Meillerwagen**. After the end of the war, large quantities of V-2 parts were seized by the United States and Russia.

Navaho.
—U.S. Air Force photograph

NAVAHO (U.S.)

Type: Surface-to-surface (air breather).

Military service and designation: Air Force (SM-64).

Status at time dropped: R&D.

Planned deployment: Location — SAC bases in continental United States.

Performance: Range — 5,500 nautical miles. Ceiling — about 50,000 ft.

Specifications: Length — 90 ft. Launch weight — about 300,000 lbs. Guidance — inertial. Warhead — nuclear. Propulsion — liquid (first stage) and ramjet (second stage).

Principal contractors: Prime — NAA. Frame — NAA. Guidance — NAA. Propulsion — NAA (first stage); Curtis-Wright (second stage).

History: R&D began in 1946. The program was canceled in 1957 on grounds that an air-breathing intercontinental missile had been made obsolete by new air defense missiles and the ICBM. However, the Navaho program contributed much to rocket technology. The engines for such missiles as Redstone, Atlas and Thor were based on Navaho work. Morever, the Navaho inertial navigation system — later to be called SINS — made the Polaris submarine possible. Total cost of the Navaho program: about 700 million dollars.

Jupiter.
—U.S. Army photograph

JUPITER (U.S.)

Type: IRBM, surface-to-surface (fixed base).

Military service and designation: Air Force and Army (SM-78).

Status at time dropped: Operational.

Deployment: Location — Italy and Turkey. Total squadrons authorized — three (two in Italy manned by Italian troops, one in Turkey manned by Turkish troops). Squadron strength — 15 missiles. Total authorized missiles on launchers — 45.

Performance: Range — 1,500 nautical miles. Speed — 10,000 m.p.h. Apogee — 380 miles.

Specifications: Length — 58 ft. Diameter — 8.75 ft. Launch weight — 150,000 lbs. Guidance — inertial. Warhead — nuclear. Propulsion — liquid (LOX and RP-1). Stages — 1. Total thrust — 150,000 lbs.

Principal contractors: Prime — Chrysler. Frame — Chrysler. Guidance — Ford Instrument. Propulsion — Rocketdyne. Re-entry vehicle — Goodyear, CTL.

History: The Army Ballistic Missile Agency developed the Jupiter in a dog-eat-dog competition with the Air Force's Thor. R&D began about 1955 as an outgrowth of work on the Redstone by the Army's noted team of German rocket experts at the Redstone Arsenal in Huntsville, Alabama. The Jupiter was the first United States IRBM to be successfully launched. The date: May 31, 1957. The Jupiter also carried the first United States full-scale nose cone down the Atlantic Missile Range in May 1958. The missile finally was turned over to the Air Force for deployment that same year. It became ready for military deployment in 1959 and operational in northern Italy in 1961. Meantime, Jupiters also played a major role in the early phases of United States space exploration. A Juno II, a space booster using Jupiter as a first stage, discovered the second Van Allen radiation belt on December 6, 1958, in an attempt to reach escape velocity that failed; another Juno II placed the Pioneer IV satellite in orbit around the sun in March 1959 and a third the Explorer VII satellite in orbit around the earth the following October.

RASCAL (U.S.)

Type: Air-to-surface.

Military service and designation: Air Force (GAM-63).

Status at time dropped: Late R&D.

Planned deployment: Location — to be carried by B-47 jet bombers.

Performance: Range — about 100 nautical miles. Speed — Mach 1.5.

Specifications: Length — 32 ft. Diameter — 4 ft. Launch weight — 13,000 lbs. Guidance — radio command. Warhead — nuclear. Propulsion — liquid (LOX and alcohol). Stages — 1. Thrust — 12,000 lbs. (3 engines at 4,000 lbs. each).

Rascal.

—U.S. Air Force photograph

Principal contractors: Prime — BTL. Frame — Bell. Guidance — BTL, RCA, and Texas Instruments. Propulsion — BTL.

History: R&D began in late 1940's. The Rascal was in production when the program was canceled in 1958.

SNARK (U.S.)

Type: Surface-to-surface (air breather).

Military service and designation: Air Force (SM-62).

Status at time dropped: Operational.

Deployment: Location — Presque Isle AFB, Presque Isle, Maine. Total squadrons — 1. Squadron strength — 30 missiles.

Performance: Range — 5,500 nautical miles. Speed — Mach .94. Ceiling — more than 50,000 ft.

Specifications: Length — 67.2 ft. Diameter — 5 ft. Wingspan — 42 ft. Launch weight — 59,936 lbs. Guidance — stellar-inertial. Warhead — nuclear. Propulsion — solid (two motors); J-57 turbojet. Stages — 2. Thrust — 33,000 lbs. (each solid motor); 10,500 lbs. (turbojet).

Principal contractors: Prime — Northrop. Frame — Northrop. Guidance — Northrop. Propulsion — Allegany (first stage); Pratt & Whitney (second stage). Launcher — Northrop.

History: R&D began in 1947. The first and only Snark squadron became initially operational at Presque Isle AFB in 1959. The Snark was dropped from SAC in June 1961. Although Snark carried a very large warhead, the missile's speed and altitude made it obsolescent in the age of ICBM's and made the cost of maintaining one squadron difficult to justify. The Snark was a good missile that came too late. Total cost of the program: 677 million dollars.

Snark.

REGULUS I (U.S.)

Type: Surface-to-surface (air breathing).

Military service and designation: Navy (RGM-6).

Status: Operational.

Deployment: Location — aboard five submarines (**U.S.S. Growler, U.S.S. Barbero, U.S.S. Grayback, U.S.S. Tunny,** and nuclear-powered **U.S.S. Halibut**) and two cruisers (**U.S.S. Los Angeles** and **U.S.S. Helena**). Missiles per submarine — 2.

Performance: Range — 500 nautical miles. Speed — about 600 m.p.h. Ceiling — about 40,000 ft. (Regulus can be launched only from the sea's surface.)

Specifications: Length — 34 ft. Diameter — 4.5 ft. Wingspan — 21 ft. Launch weight — 14,000 lbs. Guidance — radio command or inertial. Warhead — nuclear. Propulsion — solid and turbojet (J33-18). Stages — 2. Thrust — 66,000 lbs. (solid booster); 4,600 lbs. (turbojet sustainer).

Principal contractors: Prime — LTV. Frame — LTV. Guidance — Sperry. Propulsion — Aerojet (booster); Allison (sustainer).

History: R&D began in 1946. Regulus I became initially operational in 1954. The last of more than 500 were delivered in 1958 and production was ended. A much improved Regulus II was developed, but the Navy canceled the program in 1958 for budgetary reasons and because of the great promise seen in the far more advanced Polaris. However, some Regulus II's have been produced for use as drones. The Regulus II drone is designated KD2A-1.

Regulus I's aboard the submarine **Tunny** at San Diego, Calif.

The last of the missiles were removed from submarines in August 1965, and the submarines were returned to regular sea duty.

95

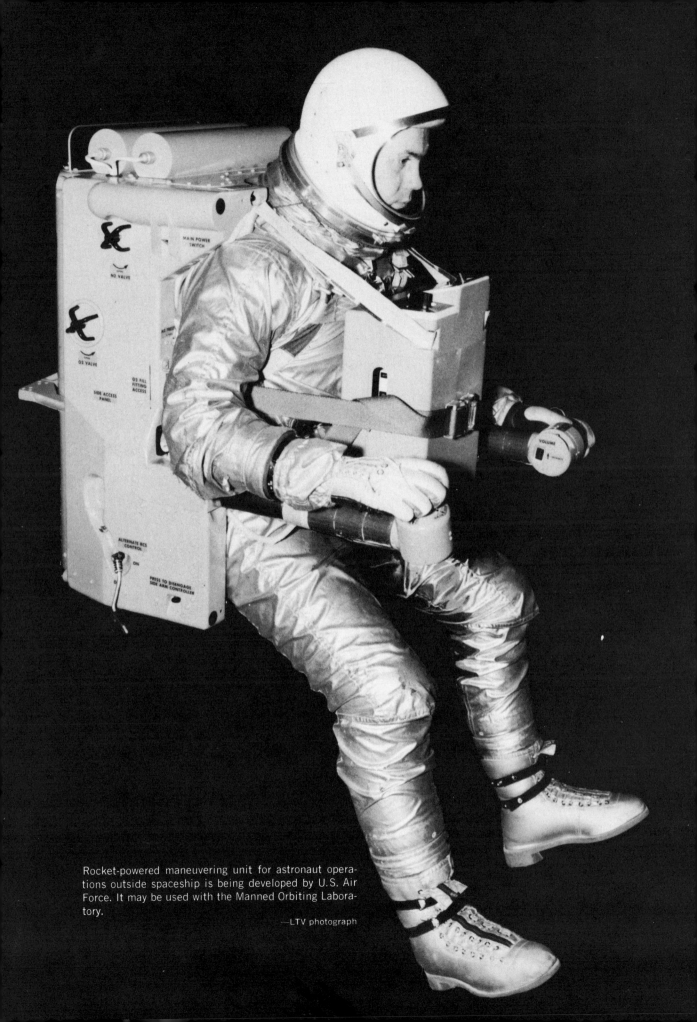

Rocket-powered maneuvering unit for astronaut operations outside spaceship is being developed by U.S. Air Force. It may be used with the Manned Orbiting Laboratory.

—LTV photograph

8

SPACE-MISSILE GUIDE

PRINCIPAL MANNED SPACECRAFT SYSTEMS

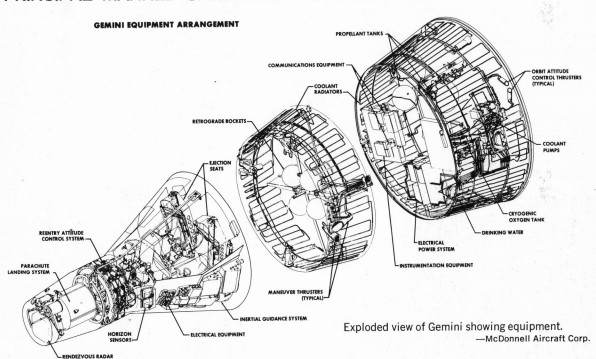

GEMINI EQUIPMENT ARRANGEMENT

PROPELLANT TANKS

COMMUNICATIONS EQUIPMENT

COOLANT RADIATORS

RETROGRADE ROCKETS

ORBIT ATTITUDE CONTROL THRUSTERS (TYPICAL)

EJECTION SEATS

COOLANT PUMPS

REENTRY ATTITUDE CONTROL SYSTEM

PARACHUTE LANDING SYSTEM

CRYOGENIC OXYGEN TANK

DRINKING WATER

ELECTRICAL POWER SYSTEM

INSTRUMENTATION EQUIPMENT

MANEUVER THRUSTERS (TYPICAL)

INERTIAL GUIDANCE SYSTEM

HORIZON SENSORS

ELECTRICAL EQUIPMENT

RENDEZVOUS RADAR

Exploded view of Gemini showing equipment.
—McDonnell Aircraft Corp.

Command module: Contains the astronaut cabin, control systems, navigation and communications equipment, radar and parachutes for landing. Teardrop-shaped Apollo is constructed of aluminum honeycomb. The base contains a beryllium heat shield covered with an ablative epoxy resin which melts away during re-entry.

Abort escape: U.S. craft have either of two systems for saving the astronauts during the earth-to-orbit flight phase. Gemini craft employ parachute-equipped ejection seats which can fire the men up and away from the capsule in the event of booster failure. Such seats are possible because the Titan II's propellants are not highly explosive, like the liquid oxygen and liquid hydrogen used by Apollo-Saturn rockets. To protect astronauts from an explosive shock wave, rockets attached to a tower on top of the Apollo are capable of pulling the whole command module free of the booster. The astronauts inside would trigger the capsule's

97

three parachutes to make the landing. Apollo does not have ejection seats.

Service module: Comparable to an engine room of a ship, this part of the craft holds, in an upper section, the retrorockets to de-orbit the spacecraft. The lower section contains stores of oxygen, pumps, batteries, fuel cells, electronic equipment, and propellants to operate attitude control thruster rockets. The Apollo service module also contains a restartable 22,000-lb.-thrust rocket engine for major maneuvers and propellants to run it.

Environmental control: All the equipment associated with keeping the astronauts alive. This includes oxygen supplies, air conditioning, management of moisture and body wastes, and the purification of the cabin atmosphere. Fuel cells, used to supply electrical power, also provide drinking water as a by-product.

Spacesuits: For strictly in-cabin use, spacesuits are designed much like the pressure suits worn by jet aircraft pilots. However, when worn in space they must be constructed much like spacecraft — strong, leakproof, and self-sustaining. The suit for Apollo explorers comes equipped with a bio-pak, a unit that is worn externally on the back and contains a miniaturized environmental control system able to sustain a man for an hour or two. Apollo suits also have a vest-like outer garment to help ward off radiation and micrometeoroids.

PRINCIPAL MISSILE SYSTEMS

Propulsion: The engines, internal fuel tanks, pumps, igniter, and related equipment that provide the thrust to propel the vehicle through all phases of powered flight. A rocket is powered by the combustion of an oxidizer and a fuel. In liquid-fueled rockets the oxidizer and fuel are stored separately and pumped simultaneously into the combustion chamber. In solid-fueled rockets the oxidizer and fuel are combined in a solid mass. This burns inside the rocket case in which it is stored. Complex internal "plumbing" is eliminated. New liquid rockets have been simplified so that it is now possible to keep the oxidizer and fuel stored in the rocket for long periods, thereby eliminating the need for fueling at the time of firing.

Guidance: The control mechanism which directs the missile to its target. Guidance systems generally are built around a gyroscope and a computer. The systems can be internal, external, or both. In an inertial system the gyro and computer are contained in the missile; in a radio command system the computer is on the ground.

Re-entry vehicle: The tip, or nose cone, of the missile, containing the warhead, the arming and fusing mechanism, and material for protecting the warhead from the heat generated by friction as it strikes the atmosphere at high speed.

Frame: The external structure of the missile.

Ground support equipment (GSE): All fueling, electronic, and mechanical equipment necessary to the successful launching of a missile or spacecraft.

GLOSSARY OF SPACE-MISSILE TERMS

Ablation: Melting of nose cone material during re-entry of a missile or spacecraft, dissipating the heat.

Air breather: A missile propelled by fuel oxidized by air from the atmosphere.

ALBM: Air-launched ballistic missile.

Aphelion: The point in an elliptical orbit around the sun that is farthest from the sun.

Apogee: The point at which a satellite in orbit is farthest from its launching point.

Black box: A term used to refer usually to an electronic component unit.

Circular error probable (CEP): The radius of a circle within which half of any given number of missiles are expected to fall.

ECM: Electronic countermeasures, used to confuse enemy radar and guidance systems.

Escape velocity: The speed a vehicle must attain to overcome a gravitational field. The escape velocity from the earth is 36,700 feet per second (about 25,000 miles per hour).

G-force: Force exerted upon an object by gravity. One G is the gravitational force on an object at sea level on the earth.

Grain: The body of a solid propellant used in a rocket.

HE: Conventional high explosive.

Heat sink: A structural contrivance used in some re-entry vehicles for the absorption of heat, keeping it from critical parts.

Hypersonic: Speeds faster than five times the speed of sound (Mach 5 plus).

ICBM: Intercontinental ballistic missile. (Range: 5,500 to more than 9,000 nautical miles.)

Ion engine: A spacecraft engine which achieves thrust from a stream of electrically energized atomic particles.

IR (Infrared): A system for guidance or reconnaissance based on infrared heat sources.

IRBM: Intermediate-range ballistic missile. (Range: about 1,500 nautical miles.)

JP: Jet fuels.

Kiloton: An explosive force equivalent to 1,000 tons of TNT.

LOX: Liquid oxygen, a basic oxidizer for rockets.

Mach: A unit of speed equal to the speed of sound in the medium in which an object is moving. (The speed of sound in air at sea level is 720 feet per second.)

Megaton: An explosive force equivalent to 1,000,000 tons of TNT.

Miniaturize: To reduce greatly in size. Usually used in regard to electronic equipment.

Operational system: A missile or space weapon that

can be used to attack an enemy target or accomplish its specific mission—in contrast to a research and development vehicle.

Orbital bomber: A spacecraft capable of orbiting the earth one or more times, delivering bombs on target, and returning to its base.

Perigee: The point at which a satellite in orbit is closest to its launch point.

Perihelion: The point on an elliptical orbit around the sun that is nearest the sun.

R&D (RDT&E): Research and development (or research, development, test and evaluation).

Reaction time: The time needed to launch a missile or spacecraft after receiving the order to do so. Most reaction times are measured against approximately 30 minutes—the time it takes an ICBM to travel 5,500 nautical miles.

Rendezvous: The technique of bringing together vehicles in orbit for a variety of purposes including fabrication of space stations, logistics and launch support for space flights.

Retrorocket: A rocket providing thrust in a direction opposite to the motion of a spacecraft—generally used to slow down a vehicle for re-entry or to correct the flight attitude. It is not considered part of the propulsion system.

RP: Rocket fuels primarily made of kerosene.

SAGE: Semi-automatic ground environment, an electronic air defense system that directs missiles and planes to attacking aircraft.

Strategic missile: A missile designed to destroy strategic targets, such as the enemy's long-range striking forces and basic military power.

Tactical missile: A missile designed to destroy such tactical targets as tanks, pillboxes, enemy strong points, ships, submarines.

Telemetry: The radio link between a missile or spacecraft and ground stations by which information about the flight is transmitted.

Thrust: The force, usually expressed in pounds, exerted on a missile or spacecraft by the combustion of its rocket propellant.

Transtage: A small rocket stage attached to a satellite. The rocket engines are capable of multiple restarts on command from the ground and make it possible to change the orbital path of a satellite as well as its apogee and perigee.

Van Allen radiation belts: Two doughnut-shaped belts of high-energy charged particles surrounding the earth. Their minimum altitude ranges from approximately 100 miles near the magnetic poles to more than 1,000 miles at the equator. The maximum altitude is approximately 40,000 miles.

Warhead: The payload of a missile, containing a nuclear bomb, a conventional high explosive (HE), or chemical or biological agents.

Wire-guided: A missile guidance system (particularly antitank) which operates by sending electrical impulses over a fine wire payed out by the missile in flight.

PRINCIPAL SPACE-MISSILE RANGES OF THE WORLD

Aberporth Missile Range (Britain)	Aberporth, Wales
Atlantic Underwater Missile Test & Evacuation Center (AUTEC) (U.S.)	Exuma, Bahama Islands
Centre Interarmée d'Essais d'Engins Spéciaux (France)	Colomb-Bechar, Algeria
Eastern Test Range (ETR) (U.S.)	Cape Kennedy, Fla.
French Guiana Test Range (France)	Cayenne, French Guiana
Gulf Test Range (U.S.)	Eglin AFB, Fla.
Joint Services Test Range (Britain)	South Uist, Outer Hebrides
Michikawa Beach Test Facility (Japan)	Akita, Honshu
Rocket Research Station (Canada-U.S.)	Ft. Churchill, Manitoba
Salto di Quirra (Italy)	Sardinia
Soviet Missile Test Range (U.S.S.R.)	Tyura Tam, Kazakh
Wallops Island Station (U.S.)	Wallops Island, Va.
Weapons Research Establishment Range (Australia-Britain)	Woomera, South Australia
Western Test Range (WTR) (U.S.)	Pt. Mugu, Calif.
White Sands Missile Range (WSMR) (U.S.)	Las Cruces, N.M.

PRINCIPAL CONTRACTORS AND GOVERNMENT AGENCIES

ABBREVIATION	FULL NAME	COUNTRY
AC Spark Plug	A. C. Spark Plug Division of General Motors Corp.	U.S.
AEC	Atomic Energy Commission	U.S.
Aerojet	Aerojet-General Corp., General Tire & Rubber Co.	U.S.
Aeronutronic	Aeronutronic Division of the Ford Motor Co.	U.S.
AFSC	Air Force Systems Command	U.S.
Allegany	Allegany Ballistics Laboratory	U.S.
Allison	Allison Division of General Motors Corp.	U.S.
AMF	American Machine & Foundry Corp.	U.S.
APL	Applied Physics Lab, Johns Hopkins University	U.S.
ASD	Aeronautical Systems Division, AFSC	U.S.
Autonetics	Autonetics Division, NAA	U.S.
Avco	Avco Corp.	U.S.
Avro	A. V. Roe & Co., Ltd.	Britain
Ball Brothers	Ball Brothers Research Corp.	U.S.
Bell	Bell Aerospace Corp., Inc.	U.S.
Bendix	The Bendix Corp.	U.S.
Boeing	The Boeing Co.	U.S.
Boelkow	Boelkow Entwicklungen	West Germany
Bombrini	Bombrini Parodi-Delfino S.p.A.	Italy
Bristol Aircraft	Bristol Aircraft, Ltd.	Britain
Bristol Siddeley	Bristol Siddeley Engines, Ltd.	Britain
Brown, Boveri	Brown, Boveri & Co.	Switzerland
BTL	Bell Telephone Laboratories, Inc.	U.S.
Burroughs	Burroughs Corp.	U.S.
Chrysler	Chrysler Corp.	U.S.
Contraves	Contraves AG and Oerlikon Machine Tool Works Buhrle & Co.	Switzerland
Convair	General Dynamics/Astronautics Division of General Dynamics Corp.	U.S.
CTL	CTL Division, Studebaker-Packard Corp.	U.S.
Curtis-Wright	Curtis-Wright Corp.	U.S.
DEFA	Direction des Etudes et Fabrications d'Armement	France
de Havilland	The de Havilland Aircraft Co., Ltd.	Britain
Douglas	Douglas Aircraft Co., Inc.	U.S.
Elliott	Elliott Bros., Ltd.	Britain
Emerson Electric	Emerson Electric Manufacturing Co.	U.S.
English Electric	English Electric Aviation Co., Ltd.	Britain
Fabrica Militar	Fabrica Militar de Aviones	Argentina
Fairey	The Fairey Co., Ltd.	Britain
Ferranti	Ferranti, Ltd.	Britain
FMC	FMC Corp.	U.S.
Ford Instrument	Ford Instrument Co., Sperry Rand Corp.	U.S.
FTL	Federal Telephone Laboratories	U.S.
Fuji	Fuji Precision Machinery Co., Ltd.	Japan
Garrett	The Garrett Corp.	U.S.
GD	General Dynamics Corp.	U.S.
GE	General Electric Co.	U.S.
Gilfillan	Gilfillan Bros., Inc.	U.S.
Goodyear	Goodyear Aircraft Corp.	U.S.
Grumman	Grumman Aircraft Engineering Corp.	U.S.
Hercules	Hercules Powder Co.	U.S.
Hesse-Eastern	Hesse-Eastern Division of Flightex Fabrics, Inc.	U.S.
Hotchkiss-Brandt	Hotchkiss-Brandt	France
Hughes	Hughes Aircraft Co.	U.S.
IBM	International Business Machines Corp.	U.S.
JPL	Jet Propulsion Laboratory (NASA)	U.S.
Kawasaki	Kawasaki Kokuki Kogyu Kabushiki Kaisha	Japan
Kearfott	Kearfott Division of General Precision, Inc.	U.S.
Koengsberg	Koengsberg Vapenfabrikk	Norway
Librascope	Librascope Division of General Precision, Inc.	U.S.

ABBREVIATION	FULL NAME	COUNTRY
LTV	LTV Aerospace Corp.	U.S.
Lockheed	Lockheed Aircraft Corp.	U.S.
Marconi	Marconi Instruments	Italy
Marquardt	The Marquardt Corp.	U.S.
Marshall Center	Marshall Space Flight Center (NASA)	U.S.
Martin	The Martin Co.	U.S.
MATRA	Société Générale de Mécanique Aviation, Traction	France
Maxson	Maxson Electronics Corp.	U.S.
McDonnell	McDonnell Aircraft Corp.	U.S.
Minneapolis-Honeywell	Minneapolis-Honeywell Regulator Co.	U.S.
MIT	Massachusetts Institute of Technology	U.S.
Mitsubishi	Shin Mitsubishi Jukogyo Kabushiki Kaisha	Japan
Mitsubishi Electric	Mitsubishi Denki K. Kaisha	Japan
NAA	North American Aviation, Inc.	U.S.
NASA	National Aeronautics and Space Administration	U.S.
Nord	Nord Aviation	France
Norris Thermador	Norris Thermador Co.	U.S.
Northrop	Northrop Corp.	U.S.
Nortronics	Nortronics Division of Northrop Corp.	U.S.
NOTS	Naval Ordnance Test Station, China Lake, Calif.	U.S.
NPP	Naval Propellant Plant	U.S.
Oerlikon	Oerlikon Machine Tool Works Buhrle & Co.	Switzerland
Philco	Philco Corp.	U.S.
Pratt & Whitney	Pratt & Whitney Aircraft Division of United Aircraft Corp.	U.S.
Raytheon	Raytheon Co.	U.S.
RCA	Radio Corporation of America	U.S.
Remington Rand Univac	Remington Rand Univac Division of Sperry Rand Corp.	U.S.
Reynolds Metals	Reynolds Metals Co.	U.S.
Robotbyran	Swedish Guided Weapons Bureau	Sweden
Rocketdyne	Rocketdyne Division of North American Aviation, Inc.	U.S.
Rolls-Royce	Rolls-Royce, Ltd.	Britain
RSAFRE	Royal Swedish Armed Forces Research Establishment	Sweden
Ruelle Arsenal	Ruelle Naval Arsenal	France
Ryan	Ryan Aeronautical Co.	U.S.
Saab	Svenska Aeroplan Aktiebolaget	Sweden
Sangamo	Sangamo Electric Co.	U.S.
SEPR	Société d'Etude de la Propulsion par Réaction	France
SEREB	Société pour l'Etude et la Réalisation d'Engins Balistiques	France
Short Bros.	Short Bros. & Harland, Ltd.	Britain
SIAL	Société Industrielle d'Aviation Latecoère	France
SISPRE	Societá Italiana Sviluppo Propulsione e Reazione	Italy
Sperry	Sperry Rand Corp.	U.S.
Sperry Gyroscope	Sperry Gyroscope Co. (of Sperry Rand Corp.)	U.S.
Sperry Utah	Sperry Utah Co. Division of Sperry Rand Corp.	U.S.
STL	Space Technology Laboratories, Inc.	U.S.
Sud	Sud Aviation	France
Summers Gyro	Summers Gyroscope Co.	U.S.
Systron-Donner	Systron-Donner, Inc.	U.S.
Texas Instruments	Texas Instruments, Inc.	U.S.
Thiokol	Thiokol Chemical Corp.	U.S.
TRW	Thompson Ramo Wooldridge Corp.	U.S.
United Aircraft	United Aircraft Corp.	U.S.
Universal Match	Universal Match Co.	U.S.
Vickers	Vickers-Armstrongs, Ltd.	Britain
Western Electric	Western Electric Co., Inc.	U.S.
Westinghouse	Westinghouse Electric Corp.	U.S.
W. G. Armstrong	Sir W. G. Armstrong Whitworth Aircraft, Ltd.	Britain